THE TIMES TOP 100 GRADUATE EMPLOYERS

The definitive guide to the leading employers
recruiting graduates during 2014-2015.

HIGH FLIERS

HIGH FLIERS PUBLICATIONS LTD
IN ASSOCIATION WITH THE TIMES

Published by High Fliers Publications Limited
King's Gate, 1 Bravingtons Walk, London N1 9AE
Telephone: 020 7428 9100 *Web:* www.Top100GraduateEmployers.com

Editor Martin Birchall
Publisher Gill Thomas
Production Director Robin Burrows
Portrait Photography Sarah Merson

The Times Top 100 Graduate Employers is based on research results
from *The UK Graduate Careers Survey 2014*, produced by High Fliers
Research Ltd.

The greatest care has been taken in compiling this book. However, no
responsibility can be accepted by the publishers or compilers for the
accuracy of the information presented.

Where opinion is expressed it is that of the author or advertiser and
does not necessarily coincide with the editorial views of High Fliers
Publications Limited or *The Times* newspaper.

Printed and bound in Italy by L.E.G.O. S.p.A.

A CIP catalogue record for this book
is available from the British Library.
ISBN 978-0-9559257-5-7

Contents

	Page
Foreword	5
Compiling the Top 100 Graduate Employers	11
Understanding the Graduate Job Market	19
Successful Job Hunting	27
Making the Most of Work Experience	39
Fifteen Years of Researching Britain's Top Employers	49

Employer Entries

	Page		Page		Page
Accenture	60	E.ON	122	Metropolitan Police	180
Airbus	62	EDF Energy	124	MI5 – The Security Service	182
Aldi	64	European Commission (EU Careers)	126	Microsoft	184
Allen & Overy	66	ExxonMobil	128	Mondelēz International	186
Arcadia Group	68	EY	130	Morgan Stanley	188
Army	70	Foreign & Commonwealth Office	132	Morrisons	190
Arup	72	Freshfields Bruckhaus Deringer	134	Newton Europe	192
Asda	74	Frontline	136	NGDP for Local Government	194
Atkins	76	GlaxoSmithKline	138	NHS	196
Baker & McKenzie	78	Goldman Sachs	140	Norton Rose Fulbright	198
Bank of America Merrill Lynch	80	Google	142	Oxfam	200
Barclays	82	Grant Thornton	144	Penguin Random House	202
BBC	84	Herbert Smith Freehills	146	Procter & Gamble	204
BlackRock	86	Hogan Lovells	148	PwC	206
Bloomberg	88	HSBC	150	Rolls-Royce	208
Boots	90	IBM	152	Royal Air Force	210
Boston Consulting Group	92	Jaguar Land Rover	154	Royal Bank of Scotland Group	212
BP	94	John Lewis Partnership	156	Royal Navy	214
British Airways	96	J.P.Morgan	158	Sainsbury's	216
British Sugar	98	KPMG	160	Savills	218
BT	100	L'Oréal	162	Shell	220
Cancer Research UK	102	Lidl	164	Siemens	222
Centrica	104	Linklaters	166	Sky	224
Citi	106	Lloyd's	168	Slaughter and May	226
Civil Service Fast Stream	108	Lloyds Banking Group	170	Teach First	228
Clifford Chance	110	Marks & Spencer	172	Tesco	230
Credit Suisse	112	Mars	174	Transport for London	232
Deloitte	114	McDonald's	176	UBS	234
Diageo	116	McKinsey & Company	178	Unilever	236
DLA Piper	118			WPP	238
Dyson	120				

Foreword

By **Martin Birchall**
Editor, *The Times Top 100 Graduate Employers*

Welcome to the sixteenth edition of *The Times Top 100 Graduate Employers*, your guide to Britain's leading employers recruiting graduates in 2014-2015.

Over the last twelve months, the graduate job market has finally recovered to its pre-recession peak. It has taken seven years to get there, but graduate vacancies in 2014 increased by almost 12 per cent year-on-year, the largest annual rise for four recruiting seasons, taking graduate recruitment back to the same level as in 2007.

Although most of the country's top employers continued hiring graduates through the worst of the recession, nearly a quarter of all entry-level vacancies were cut in 2008 and 2009. Recruitment rebounded during the following two years but graduate vacancies stalled again in 2012 before a further modest increase in 2013.

The sharp rise in recruitment in 2014 provided more opportunities for graduates from the 'Class of 2014' in eleven out of thirteen major employment sectors compared with vacancies in 2013. The strongest growth was recorded at the country's top consulting firms, accounting & professional firms, and engineering & industrial companies. And in three key employment areas – retailing, IT & telecommunications and the public sector –

" Employers expect to increase their graduate intake by 5.3 per cent during the 2014-2015 recruitment season. "

the number of graduates recruited in 2014 was actually more than 50 per cent higher than it was seven years ago.

In many ways, this welcome upturn in graduate employment mirrors Britain's wider economy which officially emerged from 'depression' in the summer of 2014, marking the point at which the country's national output exceeded the level it reached before the onset of the recession in mid-2008.

According to the Office for National Statistics, the British economy grew by more than three per cent over the last twelve months and is now averaging almost one per cent growth each quarter, a faster growth rate than other major economies such as the US, Canada and Germany.

This encouraging trend – both in the graduate job market and from the economy beyond – seems to be filtering through to the mood on campus too. The latest research with student job hunters shows that 42 per cent of final year students from the 'Class of 2014' expected to join the graduate job market straight after leaving university, one of the highest proportions recorded since the late 1990s. And an unprecedented number of finalists began researching their career options in the first or second year of their studies, determined to get a head start in the search for their first graduate job after university.

If you're one of the 365,000 finalists due to graduate in the summer of 2015, then the outlook is very encouraging too. Employers featured within this edition of *The Times Top 100 Graduate Employers* expect to increase their graduate intake by a further 5.3 per cent during the 2014-2015 recruitment season.

Around the UK, up to ten thousand employers are expecting to recruit graduates in the year ahead and more than six hundred organisations have already confirmed that they will be holding recruitment events on campus. With so many different types of employment and graduate jobs on offer, how then can prospective employers be assessed and ranked?

To find out, we interviewed 18,336 final year students who graduated from universities across the UK in the summer of 2014, and asked them "Which employer do you think offers the best opportunities for graduates?". Between them, the 'Class of 2014' named organisations in every major employment sector – the country's best-known retailers, top City investment banks,

management consulting firms, leading charities, media organisations, and the 'Big Four' accounting & professional services firms. The one hundred employers who were mentioned most often during the research form *The Times Top 100 Graduate Employers* for 2014-2015.

This book is therefore a celebration of the employers who are judged to offer the brightest prospects for graduates. Whether through the perceived quality of their training programmes, the business success that they enjoy, the scale of their organisations, or by the impression that their recruitment promotions have made – these are the employers that are most attractive to university-leavers in 2014.

The Times Top 100 Graduate Employers won't necessarily identify which organisation is right for you – only you can decide that. But it is an invaluable reference if you want to discover what Britain's leading employers have to offer. Leaving university and finding your first graduate job can be a daunting process but it is one of the most important steps you'll ever take. Having a thorough understanding of the range of opportunities available must be a good way to start.

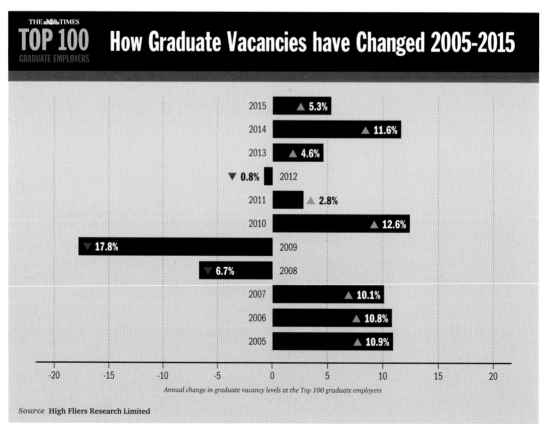

THE TIMES
TOP 100 **How Graduate Vacancies have Changed 2005-2015**
GRADUATE EMPLOYERS

Annual change in graduate vacancy levels at the Top 100 graduate employers

Source **High Fliers Research Limited**

There's a
real sense of ownership.
You can't fake anything or only operate at 90%.
It's a lifestyle not just a job.

Graduate Area Manager Programme

I think everyone's waking up to the fresh vibrancy of Aldi. I was canoeing down a fjord in New Zealand and these Americans were like 'Hey do you work for Aldi? We LOVE Aldi!'. It was so funny. Thing is, there's lots to love, especially as a graduate. It's very fast-paced with plenty of variety. I admire Aldi's frugality and efficiency; everything's just incredibly well-managed. We're all working in harmony and there's a strong sense of combined purpose. If you really want this (and you're prepared to work hard) you develop skills for life. And I like that.

aldirecruitment.co.uk/graduates

LIKE NO OTHER

This is

My **KPMG**

Katharine, Graduate Trainee

cutting through complexity

Compiling the Top 100 Graduate Employers

By **Gill Thomas**
Publisher, High Fliers Publications

B ritain's rapidly-growing economy means that the prospects for university-leavers are now the best they've been for more than a decade and up to ten thousand employers, large and small, are set to hire new graduates from the country's top universities during the 2014-2015 recruitment season.

With such a promising range of employment options, trying to find the organisation that is 'right' for you can be quite a daunting challenge. How can you assess the different opportunities and decide which employers offer the best career paths? What basis can you use to evaluate so many different types of organisations and graduate roles?

It's clear there are no simple answers to these questions and no one individual employer can ever hope to be right for every graduate – everyone makes their own judgement about the organisations they want to work for and the type of job they find the most attractive.

How then can anyone produce a meaningful league table of Britain's leading graduate employers? What criteria can define whether one individual organisation is 'better' than another? To compile the new edition of *The Times Top 100 Graduate Employers*, the independent market research company, High Fliers Research,

66 For an unprecedented eleventh consecutive year, PwC has been voted the UK's number one graduate employer. 99

interviewed 18,336 final year students who left UK universities in the summer of 2014.

These finalists from the 'Class of 2014' who took part in the study were selected at random to represent the full cross-section of finalists at their universities, not just those who had already secured graduate employment. The research examined students' experiences during their search for a graduate job and asked them about their attitudes to employers.

The key question used to produce the *Top 100* was "Which employer do you think offers the best opportunities for graduates?" This question was deliberately open-ended and students were not prompted in any way.

Across the full survey sample, finalists named more than 1,300 different organisations – from the smallest local or regional employers, to some of the world's best-known companies. The responses were analysed and the one hundred organisations that were mentioned most often make up the *The Times Top 100 Graduate Employers* for 2014.

Looking at the considerable selection of answers given by finalists from the 'Class of 2014', it is clear that individual students used several different criteria to determine which employer they considered offered the best opportunities for

THE TIMES TOP 100 GRADUATE EMPLOYERS

The Times Top 100 Graduate Employers 2014

	2013				2013	
1.	1	PWC		51.	69	FOREIGN & COMMONWEALTH OFFICE
2.	3	TEACH FIRST		52.	51	MI5 – THE SECURITY SERVICE
3.	2	DELOITTE		53.	65	LOCAL GOVERNMENT
4.	6	ALDI		54.	35	SKY
5.	8	NHS		55.	90	AIRBUS
6.	5	CIVIL SERVICE		56.	49	CANCER RESEARCH UK
7.	4	KPMG		57.	62	CREDIT SUISSE
8.	11	BBC		58.	44	SLAUGHTER AND MAY
9.	10	GOOGLE		59.	47	MCDONALD'S
10.	9	JOHN LEWIS PARTNERSHIP		60.	48	ASDA
11.	7	EY		61.	92	BLACKROCK
12.	13	UNILEVER		62.	86	GRANT THORNTON
13.	12	BARCLAYS		63.	99	TRANSPORT FOR LONDON
14.	14	BP		64.	43	NESTLÉ
15.	19	GLAXOSMITHKLINE		65.	66	BANK OF AMERICA MERRILL LYNCH
16.	21	JAGUAR LAND ROVER		66.	70	SIEMENS
17.	18	GOLDMAN SACHS		67.	72	BAKER & MCKENZIE
18.	22	J.P. MORGAN		68.	88	ROYAL NAVY
19.	24	ROLLS-ROYCE		69.	53	DEUTSCHE BANK
20.	16	ACCENTURE		70.	58	EUROPEAN COMMISSION (EU CAREERS)
21.	17	HSBC		71.	59	DEPARTMENT FOR INTERNATIONAL DEVELOPMENT
22.	20	IBM		72.	57	EXXONMOBIL
23.	15	TESCO		73.	63	POLICE
24.	27	MICROSOFT		74.	89	ROYAL AIR FORCE
25.	29	SHELL		75.	98	CENTRICA
26.	23	PROCTER & GAMBLE		76.	NEW	FRONTLINE
27.	39	ARUP		77.	NEW	BRITISH SUGAR
28.	26	ARMY		78.	85	OXFAM
29.	30	MCKINSEY & COMPANY		79.	75	ARCADIA GROUP
30.	33	LLOYDS BANKING GROUP		80.	77	SANTANDER
31.	31	LIDL		81.	80	UBS
32.	36	CLIFFORD CHANCE		82.	67	PENGUIN
33.	32	MARKS & SPENCER		83.	68	HOGAN LOVELLS
34.	42	LINKLATERS		84.	78	HERBERT SMITH FREEHILLS
35.	34	ALLEN & OVERY		85.	87	LLOYD'S
36.	25	ROYAL BANK OF SCOTLAND GROUP		86.	NEW	BLOOMBERG
37.	38	MORGAN STANLEY		87.	NEW	NORTON ROSE FULBRIGHT
38.	50	WPP		88.	55	BOOTS
39.	37	SAINSBURY'S		89.	NEW	SAVILLS
40.	45	FRESHFIELDS BRUCKHAUS DERINGER		90.	64	DLA PIPER
41.	28	L'ORÉAL		91.	96	MONDELĒZ INTERNATIONAL
42.	40	APPLE		92.	73	RED BULL
43.	60	BT		93.	79	EDF ENERGY
44.	54	BOSTON CONSULTING GROUP		94.	NEW	DYSON
45.	56	BRITISH AIRWAYS		95.	NEW	E.ON
46.	41	BAE SYSTEMS		96.	76	CHANNEL 4
47.	46	CITI		97.	82	DIAGEO
48.	52	MARS		98.	94	NEWTON EUROPE
49.	61	ATKINS		99.	83	GE
50.	71	BAIN & COMPANY		100.	84	MORRISONS

Source **High Fliers Research** 18,336 final year students leaving UK universities in the summer of 2014 were asked the open-ended question 'Which employer do you think offers the best opportunities for graduates?' during interviews for *The UK Graduate Careers Survey 2014*

graduates. Some focused on employers' general reputations – their public image, their business profile or their commercial success.

Others evaluated employers based on the information they had seen during their job search – the quality of recruitment promotions, the impression formed from meeting employers' representatives, or experiences through the recruitment and selection process. Finalists also considered the level of vacancies that organisations were recruiting for as an indicator of possible employment prospects, or were influenced by employers' profiles at their university.

Many final year students, however, used the 'employment proposition' as their main guide – the quality of graduate training and development an employer offers, the starting salary and remuneration package available, and the practical aspects of a first graduate job, such as location or working hours.

Irrespective of the criteria that students used to arrive at their answer, the hardest part for many was just selecting a single organisation. To some extent, choosing two or three, or even half a dozen employers would have been much easier. But the whole purpose of the exercise was to replicate the reality that everyone faces – you can only work for one organisation. And at each stage of the graduate job search there are choices to be made as to which direction to take and which employers to pursue.

The resulting *Top 100* is a dynamic league table of the UK's most exciting and well-respected graduate recruiters in 2014. For an unprecedented eleventh consecutive year, the accounting and professional services firm, PwC, has been voted the UK's number one graduate employer, after polling 8.6 per cent of finalists' votes, its strongest result since 2010.

After eight years in second place, rival accountancy firm Deloitte has been overtaken by the widely-acclaimed Teach First scheme, which has now moved up the rankings in ten of the last eleven years since it joined the *Top 100* in 63rd place in 2003. Aldi's popular trainee area manager programme and the NHS have both returned to the top five but the Civil Service has slipped to sixth place and KPMG has dropped back to seventh place this year, its lowest ranking for more than a decade. The BBC has moved back into the top ten, just ahead of Google which has now reached

ninth place, its highest ever position since first appearing in the *Top 100* as a new entry in 85th place in 2005. But after climbing for seven years in a row, the John Lewis Partnership slips back to tenth place this year.

EY, the accountancy firm that recently rebranded from Ernst & Young, has slipped four places, taking it out of the top ten for the first time in five years. Consumer goods company Unilever has moved up to twelfth place, its highest *Top 100* rating since 2003 and Jaguar Land Rover has risen further up the rankings to join the top twenty for the first time, having climbed more than seventy places in just four years. Rolls-Royce has also achieved its best ever *Top 100* position, moving up to nineteenth place but consulting and technology company Accenture is down four places and HSBC has dropped out of the top twenty altogether, to its lowest ranking since 2001.

The highest climbers in this year's *Top 100* are led by Transport for London, which has jumped an impressive thirty-six places to 63rd place. Airbus has climbed thirty-five places to 55th position and BlackRock, a new entry in 2013, has moved up thirty-one places. But Boots, DLA Piper, Nestlé and Channel 4 have each dropped at least twenty places in the new rankings.

It has been a good year for the strategy consulting firms – McKinsey & Company has reached its highest ranking since 2001 and both the Boston Consulting Group and Bain & Company have achieved their best ever positions, appearing within the top fifty for the first time. By contrast, there have been somewhat mixed fortunes for the leading City banking and financial institutions in 2014 – half of the twelve banks featured within the new *Top 100* have slipped down the rankings but Goldman Sachs, J.P. Morgan, Lloyds Banking Group and Morgan Stanley are among those that have improved their ratings year-on-year.

Within the Armed Forces, the Army has again struggled in this year's *Top 100*, dropping a further two places to 28th place, its lowest rating so far in the league table. But the RAF is up fifteen places and the Royal Navy has jumped twenty places in the latest rankings.

There are a total of seven new entries or re-entries in this year's *Top 100*, the highest being for Frontline, the new programme recruiting graduates for children's social work that launched in autumn 2013. British Sugar and Bloomberg have both returned to the *Top 100* in 77th and 86th places respectively, after dropping out of the list last year. The law firm Norton Rose Fulbright is ranked in 87th place, and property group Savills reappears in 89th place. Engineering and technology company Dyson is ranked within the *Top 100* for the first time in 94th place, just ahead of energy company E.ON which is a re-entry in 95th place.

Organisations leaving the *Top 100* in 2014 include the Co-operative Group, Network Rail and National Grid and four graduate employers that were new or re-entries in last year's rankings – Coca-Cola, Danone, Balfour Beatty and Thomson Reuters.

This year's edition of *The Times Top 100 Graduate Employers* has produced a number of significant changes within the rankings and the results provide a unique insight into how graduates from the 'Class of 2014' rated the UK's leading employers. Almost all of these organisations are featured in the 'Employer Entry' section of this book – from page 57 onwards, you can see a two-page profile for each employer, listed alphabetically for easy reference.

The editorial part of the entry includes a short description of what the organisation does, its

opportunities for graduates and its recruitment programme for 2014-2015. A fact file for each employer gives details of the business functions that graduates are recruited for, the number of graduate vacancies on offer, likely starting salaries for 2015, their minimum academic requirements, application deadlines, the universities that the employer is intending to visit during the year, plus details of their graduate recruitment website and how to follow the employer on Facebook, Twitter and LinkedIn. The right-hand page of each employer entry contains a display advert promoting the organisation.

If you would like to find out more about any of the employers featured in *The Times Top 100 Graduate Employers*, then simply register with **www.Top100GraduateEmployers.com** – the official website showcasing the latest news and information about *Top 100* organisations.

Registration is entirely free and as well as being able to access the website, you'll receive regular email updates about the employers you are most interested in – this includes details of the careers events they're holding at your university during the year, up-and-coming job application deadlines, and the very latest business news about the organisations.

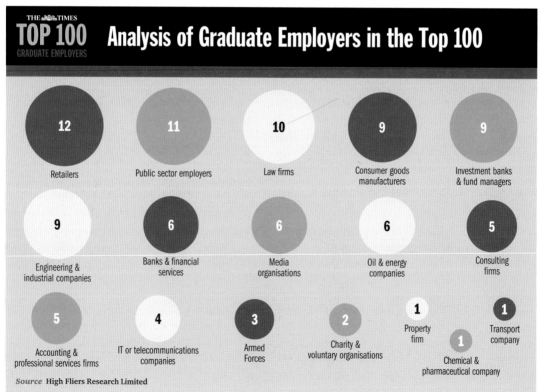

THE TIMES TOP 100 GRADUATE EMPLOYERS
Analysis of Graduate Employers in the Top 100

12 Retailers	**11** Public sector employers
10 Law firms	**9** Consumer goods manufacturers
9 Investment banks & fund managers	**9** Engineering & industrial companies
6 Banks & financial services	**6** Media organisations
6 Oil & energy companies	**5** Consulting firms
5 Accounting & professional services firms	**4** IT or telecommunications companies
3 Armed Forces	**2** Charity & voluntary organisations
1 Property firm	**1** Chemical & pharmaceutical company
1 Transport company	

Source High Fliers Research Limited

LEADERS

by Sainsbury's

The 2015 Graduate Programme

What does it really mean to be a leader? Leaders by Sainsbury's equips you with everything you need to play a critical leadership role in our business. Maybe you'll lead a fast-paced store team; maybe you'll take the lead in strategic decision-making; or maybe you'll lead the development of a new product. Whichever area you excel in, you'll be at the forefront of a great retailer, inspiring others, gaining recognition and making the most of some wonderful development opportunities.

Find out what it means to be a leader, by Sainsbury's. To apply, visit sainsburys.jobs/graduates

WE STAND OUT BECAUSE OF *YOU*

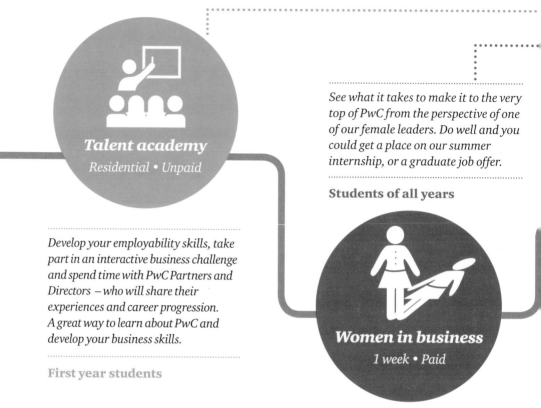

Talent academy
Residential • Unpaid

See what it takes to make it to the very top of PwC from the perspective of one of our female leaders. Do well and you could get a place on our summer internship, or a graduate job offer.

Students of all years

Develop your employability skills, take part in an interactive business challenge and spend time with PwC Partners and Directors – who will share their experiences and career progression. A great way to learn about PwC and develop your business skills.

First year students

Women in business
1 week • Paid

Boost your employability

We've got lots of different work experience programmes so you can learn more about us and boost your employability. They'll help you make an informed decision about which of our career opportunities is best for you. To find out more, visit ***www.pwc.com/uk/careers***

Take the opportunity of a lifetime

pwc

Graduate job

Summer internships
6-8 weeks • Paid

Develop business knowledge by working on client projects. In 11 months you'll have gained a deep insight into our business and developed your technical skills. This opportunity is ideal if you need to complete a placement as part of your degree, and could lead to a graduate job offer.

Sandwich/placement students

Work alongside specialists in one of our business areas. You'll work on client projects for six to eight weeks, to give you the best insight into our work. Do well and you could go back to university with a graduate job offer.

Penultimate year students

Work placement
11 months • Paid

Graduates can also join on a graduate work placement.

Nearly 40 graduates fighting over each job

Greg Hurst Education Editor

Britain's class of 2014 can expect to choose from a near-reco... of

man Sachs, carried out by High

schools, the government's communications headquarters (GCHQ), appointments to the Civil Service fast

Graduates in jobs boost

THE number of job opening

Graduate openings 'at highest level since 2007'

LEADING employers received about 39 applications for every graduate job this
... in vacancies, research

Students graduating this year face best prospects of employment since 200

Half of first-year students are already looking for job

started looking in the fir of the degree, and a furt per cent were searching they started the course

Students who took this year's poll colled made 463,000 job ap tions, up from 257,00 by those who gradua 2010. On average, nev uates expect a starting of £23,000, the poll

Top jobs chased by 39 graduates

LEADING employers have received about 39 applications for each graduate job this year, a

years.' Vacancies jumped 11.6 per cent this year, with overall recruitment returning to the
... l as 2007.

...ting had the m... ... avail...

Interns stand best chance of landing new graduate jobs

Graduate vacancie. are on the increase

TOP empl... about 39 a... every gradu... amid a rise... research su...
A study

Graduate recruitment top firms rises by 8.7%

Britain's class of 2014 can look forwa to the strongest graduate jobs marke since before the financial crisis savag the economy, new research shows.

According to the market research High Fliers Research some of Britain biggest employers, including Google

Rise in graduate vacancies 'to pre-recession levels'

By ALISON KERSHAW

...ers rec... arou...

engineering and industrial (1,650 va-

imum number of Ucas unive iff" points, which are based A-level results.

First-year student: under pressure to take on internship

Gr... Hurst Education Editor

A quarter of employers ru internships for first-year studen

Graduate job prospects best since 2007 as public sector leads recruitment

RICHARD GARNER
EDUCATION EDITOR

Job prospects for the class of 2014 – graduating this sum-mer – are as rosy as at any time since the start of the reces-

HIRING GRADUATE RECRUITERS

Trends in vacancies from 2007

leaving universities this yea are the best they have been since the sart of the recession seven years ago."

"The outlook for 2014 is sig-nificantly more upbeat," the report concluded.

The 8.7 per cent rise is th

Graduate positions with top firms set to shoot up in 201

CRAIG BROWN

GRADUATE recruitment by

saw companies slash grad vacancies by 6.7 per cent

Understanding the Graduate Job Market

By **Martin Birchall**
Managing Director, High Fliers Research

With the economic recovery in full swing and confirmation that graduate recruitment has now returned to its pre-recession levels, new graduates who left university in the summer of 2014 will have seen increasingly encouraging newspaper headlines about the graduate job market.

Britain's leading employers stepped up their graduate vacancies by a better-than-expected 11.6 per cent during the 2013-2014 university year, taking graduate recruitment back to its highest level since 2007. But a record number of vacancies were filled by graduates who had already completed work experience with employers and competition for places on the top graduate schemes remained intense, with recruiters receiving an average of thirty-nine applications per vacancy during the year.

For graduates from the 'Class of 2015', the outlook is a positive one – the latest analysis shows that vacancies at the leading graduate employers are set to increase by a further 5.3 per cent in 2015.

More than two-fifths of the organisations in *The Times Top 100 Graduate Employers* plan to hire more graduates this year than they did in 2014, a third believe they will take a similar volume of recruits, while a quarter expect to reduce their graduate intake, albeit usually by a small number of roles. Together, employers in this year's *Top 100* are advertising a total of 19,723 jobs, compared to the 18,726 graduates these organisations hired in 2014.

This year's graduate recruitment will again be dominated by the country's largest accountancy & professional services firms who are preparing to recruit 4,500 new trainees in 2015, almost a quarter of the total number of new graduate vacancies available at *Top 100* employers.

For the sixth year running, the number of graduate roles at the top engineering & industrial firms is expected to increase, taking recruitment in the sector 10 per cent higher than before the beginning of the recession in 2008.

Employers in ten of the fifteen industries and business sectors represented within the *Top 100* expect to either maintain or step up their graduate recruitment in 2015.

The best-known consumer goods manufacturers in the UK are planning to recruit a fifth more graduates in the coming year and there are increases in vacancies too at City investment banks & fund managers, oil & energy companies, Armed Forces and banking & financial services employers. Vacancy numbers in the transport and chemical

> **“** In 2015, the Teach First programme is expected to be the biggest individual employer of graduates, with 2,060 places. **”**

This is our story

Quietly doing brilliant things

ΛTKINS

"I wanted to work on some of the most prestigious engineering projects around, across a number of different industries."

Matthew

Graduate and undergraduate opportunities

£competitive pay | Opportunities across the UK

There's more to Atkins than meets the eye. We're the UK's largest engineering consultancy and the biggest multi-disciplinary consultancy in Europe. We're also the seventh largest design firm in the world with a c.£1.4 billion turnover and a global team of around 17,000 brilliant people.

Join us as a graduate or on a placement and you'll broaden your skills and help us to achieve great things, as we take on some of the most exciting engineering challenges of our time.

Amazing projects. Unique challenges. Competitive pay. Your story starts here. Discover more about our opportunities across the UK at

www.atkinsglobal.com /careers/graduates

Plan Design Enable

& pharmaceuticals sectors are unchanged year-on-year but there are likely to be slightly fewer graduate opportunities at the leading law firms, IT & telecommunications companies, consulting firms, high street retailers and media organisations in the year ahead.

Employers featured within the *Top 100* are offering an average of 200 graduate vacancies each for 2015, but a quarter of organisations plan to hire more than 250 new recruits and four employers anticipate recruiting at least 1,000 university-leavers during 2014-2015.

Whilst general recruitment remains restricted within many parts of the public sector, the eleven Government departments and agencies appearing in the latest *Top 100* rankings are planning to step up their graduate intake by more than 20 per cent in 2015 – making this the sixth time in seven years

that recruitment of graduates has increased within the public sector.

The continuing major expansion of the Teach First programme means that for the third consecutive year, its graduate recruitment targets are the largest of any organisation featured in *The Times Top 100 Graduate Employers*, with 2,060 places available in 2015. Other substantial recruiters include the accounting & professional services firms PwC and Deloitte (1,200 vacancies each), KPMG (1,000 vacancies), EY (800 vacancies), the Civil Service Fast Stream (800 vacancies) and the Army (650 vacancies).

Up to three-fifths of the employers featured in this year's Top 100 have vacancies for graduates in IT, at least half have opportunities in financial management, two-fifths are recruiting for human resources or marketing roles, over a third are hiring

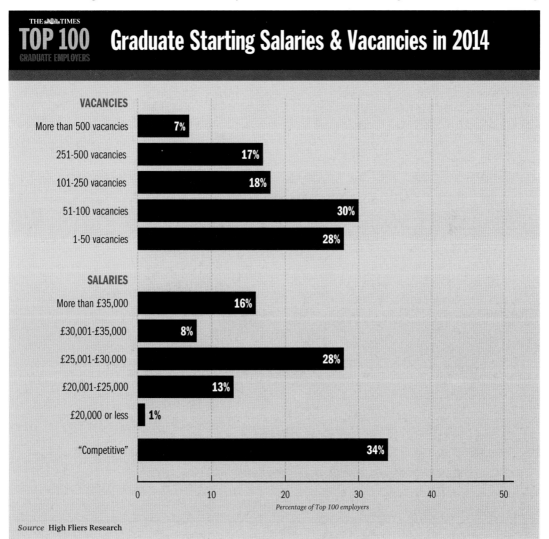

THE TIMES

TOP 100 Graduate Starting Salaries & Vacancies in 2014
GRADUATE EMPLOYERS

Source High Fliers Research

engineering or general management graduates, a quarter are looking for recruits to work in sales, research & development or purchasing, but fewer than a fifth want retail personnel or have roles in consulting.

More than eighty of the *Top 100* employers have graduate vacancies in London and over half have posts available elsewhere in the south east of England. More than half also have graduate roles in the north west of England, the south west and the Midlands. Northern Ireland, Wales and East Anglia have the fewest vacancies.

In 2014, the typical graduate starting salary available at Britain's leading employers increased for the first time since 2010, to an average of £29,500. Over half of the organisations featured in this year's edition of *The Times Top 100 Graduate Employers* have opted to leave their graduate starting salaries unchanged from 2014 rates but a number of employers – including several leading law firms, engineering & industrial companies and retailers – have announced increases to their graduate packages for 2015, typically by between £500 and £2,000 each.

A third of *Top 100* employers simply describe their salary packages for next year as "competitive" but one in six organisations – mainly investment banks, City law firms, the leading oil & energy

companies and two well-known retailers – are planning to pay starting salaries in excess of £35,000. The most generous graduate packages publicised within this edition of the *Top 100* are again at the European Commission, which offers new graduates a salary of at least £41,500, and retailer Aldi who continues to offer its recruits a sector-leading starting salary of £41,000 and an Audi A4 car.

Half the UK's leading employers now recruit graduates year-round (or in different phases during the year) and will accept applications throughout the 2014-2015 recruitment season, until all their vacancies are filled. For employers with a single application deadline, most are in either November, December or January, although the leading City law firms usually have July closing dates for their training contracts.

Two thirds of *Top 100* employers insist that applicants for their graduate programmes should have a 2.1 degree or better and over a fifth now specify a minimum UCAS tariff too, typically in the range of 260 to 340 – the equivalent of 'BCC' to 'AAB' at A-level.

So for those who make the grade, there continues to be an excellent range of career opportunities and some great starting salaries on offer from *The Times Top 100 Graduate Employers* in 2015.

THE TIMES TOP 100 GRADUATE EMPLOYERS — Graduate Vacancies at Top 100 Employers in 2015

	2014		NUMBER OF VACANCIES	% OF TOTAL VACANCIES	CHANGE SINCE 2014
1.	1	ACCOUNTANCY & PROFESSIONAL SERVICES FIRMS	4,500	22.8	▲ 1.3%
2.	2	PUBLIC SECTOR EMPLOYERS	3,852	19.5	▲ 21.9%
3.	3	INVESTMENT BANKS & FUND MANAGERS	1,895	9.6	▲ 4.8%
4.	4	ENGINEERING & INDUSTRIAL COMPANIES	1,675	8.5	▲ 8.1%
5.	5	RETAILERS	1,383	7.0	▼ 8.8%
6.	6	BANKING & FINANCIAL SERVICES	1,330	6.7	▲ 5.8%
7.	7	ARMED FORCES	1,300	6.6	▲ 12.4%
8.	9	IT & TELECOMMUNICATION COMPANIES	786	4.0	▼ 5.3%
9.	8	LAW FIRMS	750	3.8	▼ 1.8%
10.	10	CONSULTING FIRMS	570	2.9	▼ 7.6%
11.	11	OIL & ENERGY COMPANIES	535	2.7	▲ 4.1%
12.	13	MEDIA ORGANISATIONS	504	2.6	▼ 13.3%
13.	12	CONSUMER GOODS MANUFACTURERS	375	1.9	▲ 21.8%
14.	14	TRANSPORT COMPANIES	75	0.4	NO CHANGE
15.	15	CHEMICAL & PHARMACEUTICAL COMPANIES	65	0.3	NO CHANGE

Source High Fliers Research

Discover

your strengths

LOOK FOR US UNDER M

If you're looking for a fast moving, far reaching career and you have the right core strengths to branch out in all directions, you'll find what you're looking for at Morrisons. For more information find us under M. Our tailored schemes are ripe for the picking!

Morrisons.jobs/graduates

(M) **MORRISONS**

THEIR'S MORE TO TEACHING THAN YOU THINK.

Mistakes spring out at you. That's because you know the power of an apostrophe, or the wonder of an experiment, or the joy of solving an equation. You probably had a teacher who instilled this in you. What you might not know yet are the rewards that come with a teaching career, like inspiring hundreds of your students' futures, or the legacy you'll leave behind. It's the one profession that starts every other. Plus, there's a minimum starting salary of between £21k and £27k a year, depending on your location, and you can go on to earn £64k a year as a great classroom teacher. It doesn't need spelling out that it's a terrific career. If you can see yourself in teaching visit **education.gov.uk/teachtimes.**

Your Future | Their Future

Department for Education

careers@bath

focus on your future

- Choose a career
- Succeed in the selection process
- Get work experience
- Find a graduate job
- Find postgraduate study

THE UNIVERSITY
OF BATH CAREERS
GUIDE 2014

careers@bath
focus on your future · BATH

Finding a
graduate job

careers@bath
focus on your future · BATH

Interviews and
assessment centres
guide

careers@bath
focus on your future · BATH

Interviews and
assessment centres
guide

careers@bath
focus on your future · BATH

Finding a
graduate job

THE UNIVERSITY
OF BATH CAREERS
GUIDE 2014

NETWORKING

Successful Job Hunting

By **Tracey Wells**
Head of the Careers Service, University of Bath

With many of the UK's major employers now accepting applications for their graduate programmes more than a year before students leave university, and increasing numbers of organisations hiring their new graduates through internships or work experience programmes, it's never too soon to begin exploring the graduate opportunities that are available, understanding what employers are looking for and developing the skills you need to be successful in the job market.

It's a process that more and more students are starting during their first year at university and with good reason – it's not good discovering in your final year that employers in the career sector you're interested in require you to have done relevant work experience beforehand, because by that point you could have missed the chance to apply for an internship or vacation placement.

Whichever year of study you are in, a good place to begin your career preparations is the university careers service. Every university in the UK has its own careers support to help students make career decisions and guide them through their search for a graduate job. Professional careers advisers are usually available to provide one-to-one guidance, to help you to think through your options,

" Many employers run skills training sessions to help students prepare for key parts of the graduate recruitment process. "

develop your self-awareness and help you find the information you need about different career paths and opportunities.

Don't worry if you're one of the many people who have little idea of what you want to do after university – you don't need to have any firm plans or a career path mapped out before you come and talk to a careers adviser. They can work with you to understand your skills, experiences and what's important to you, as well as helping you work out how to go about exploring different career options by introducing you to the resources and assistance that is available.

Much as you might want to say to your careers adviser – "I've done this degree, I've got this experience, this is what I like doing, please tell me what I'm going to do with the rest of my life" – that isn't their role. They won't make career decisions for you or point you towards particular employers but they will challenge you to think about what it is you could be suited to and what your strengths are.

At most university careers services, careers advisers are available on either a drop-in or a book-on-the-day basis for shorter enquiries, with the possibility of longer pre-booked sessions of up to 45 minutes for more in-depth consultations and advice – check with your careers service to

Institute
and Faculty
of Actuaries

Why a career as an actuary adds up for me

❝ My job is to work out the risk of an event taking place and then to calculate what the impact of that would be for the business I'm working for.

I could be analysing weather patterns, the housing market in Brazil, London traffic trends or attendances at music festivals.

It's challenging, offers lots of opportunities for progression and it's well paid right from the start. ❞

What you'll need to become an actuary

Actuaries love numbers. A degree in maths, statistics, actuarial science, economics or a related discipline such as physics is required alongside a maths A level.

You can rely on the support of the Institute and Faculty of Actuaries. We have over 25,000 members worldwide who call on our support, information resources and networking opportunities throughout their careers.

What can I earn?

Graduate Actuarial Trainees earn £35,219.

Where can I find out more?

e: careers@actuaries.org.uk

w: www.actuaries.org.uk/becoming-actuary/
       pages/becoming-actuary

see what they offer. The autumn period can be a particularly busy time so it's worth booking your appointments as early as possible if you feel you'd benefit from a longer discussion with an adviser.

Careers services provide a wealth of information which can help you understand different employment options, such as printed careers guides, events information, contact details for alumni of the university and destination data about past graduates from individual faculties or degree courses. This can be especially useful if you're studying a non-vocational subject and are worried that it doesn't naturally lead towards any particular career direction – seeing the range of things that recent graduates from your subject have gone on to do after university can provide some helpful pointers. Some universities offer formal mentoring schemes, connecting current students with recent alumni who can provide an informal first-hand introduction to the career area they're working in.

There are also several online careers guidance tools, like the *Prospects Career Planner* which can be useful to help you understand the type of jobs or sectors you could be suited to. By answering a series of questions about yourself and your interests, you'll get a report back giving an outline of the potential careers that fit your profile. Even if you don't think the results are necessarily relevant to you or are sceptical about the types of jobs it suggests, the process of answering the questions can at least get you thinking.

If you're a fresher at university, there are a number of major employers who have insight programmes specifically for first years which are held during the Easter or summer vacations and offer an introduction to their organisation and a taster of what working in their sector would be like. This can be really valuable experience, even if the outcome is that you realise that type of employment isn't right for you. Your careers adviser can help you reflect on your experiences, positive or negative, to help you understand what it was you liked and disliked about the working environment and the roles you observed.

For penultimate year students, many of the larger employers run formal internship programmes lasting eight weeks or longer during the summer vacation before final year. Competition for places on these schemes can often be just as intense as for full-time graduate positions and the selection

process is usually equally rigorous with application deadlines early in the autumn – up to eight months before the internships actually start – and multi-stage selection processes with a series of aptitude tests, interviews and assessment centres.

But don't worry if you don't manage to secure an internship. There are many other ways of getting valuable experience and developing your employability skills while you're at university, whether it's with smaller companies, through volunteering, being an active member of a student society or taking on a position of responsibility, or enterprise activities. And doing a part-time job alongside your studies can also be a good way to get useful work experience – it may not be in the sector that you eventually want to end up working in but it's an opportunity to add to your skills and experience different workplaces.

To help you find out more about individual employers and their graduate schemes, your university careers service will typically coordinate events such as university careers fairs and employer presentations, which are usually open to students in all years. Careers fairs might be sector-specific recruitment events for areas such as engineering, finance, IT or law, or they could be general events which include a broad range of graduate employers from different industries and business sectors. There are also several national and regional graduate recruitment fairs that are held each autumn and summer.

Employers will usually send a mix of recent graduates, recruiters and sometimes more senior staff to careers fairs and so to get as much as possible out of these events, it's really important to do some preparation. Most organisers will publish a list of the employers who'll be attending careers fairs in advance, so you can draw up a list of those that most interest you and read up on them beforehand. That way you can make a good impression when you start talking to them on the day and avoid asking really obvious questions that you could have found out by looking at their graduate recruitment website. It's also worth remembering that some employers may make a note of the names of students they've been particularly impressed by, so they can look out for their applications.

Careers fairs can seem quite intimidating, especially if it's the first event you go to, so don't feel you have to go straight up to graduate recruiters

DISCOVER MORE ABOUT THE WORLD OF ADVERTISING...

DIFFERENT MINDSETS LEAD TO DIFFERENT JOB ROLES

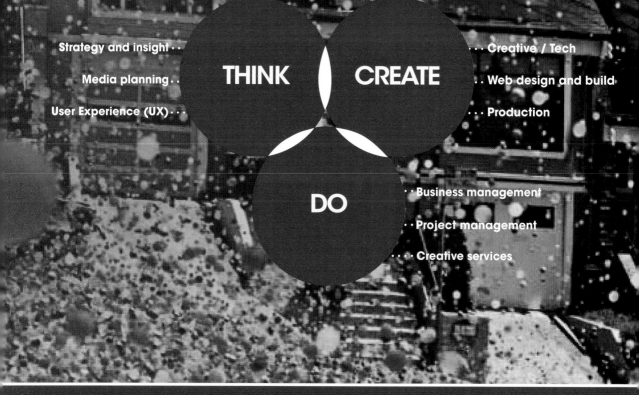

Strategy and insight · ·

Media planning · ·

User Experience (UX) · ·

THINK

CREATE

· · Creative / Tech

· · Web design and build

· · Production

DO

· · Business management

· · Project management

· · Creative services

The UK is a global centre of excellence for advertising. Advertising is the second largest sector of the UK creative industries, with an annual growth rate of 6.6%, and contributes £ 10.2bn of Gross Value Added (GVA) to the UK economy. The Institute of Practitioners in Advertising (IPA) represents the leading agencies in the sector, and provides a gateway to around 1000 graduate and school leaver job opportunities each year.

www.theadmission.co.uk

www.ipa.co.uk

and start to ask questions. If there's an employer you're interested in, see if you can listen in on somebody else's conversation, particularly if a recruiter is talking to a small group of students – what they're talking about could be just as helpful without you having to ask your own questions.

Employer presentations offer the chance to spend more time with the organisations that really interest you. Different employers take different approaches to their events – some are quite formal, with a PowerPoint presentation, a talk and the chance for questions at the end. Others include more of a networking element, often over refreshments, with the opportunity to chat to their graduates to find out what it's really like to work there and hear about the different roles available. To ensure you're using your time effectively, be selective about the number of events you attend and prepare the questions you want to ask beforehand.

Increasingly, many employers also run skills training sessions to help students prepare for key parts of the graduate recruitment process or develop their business skills and abilities. At many universities employers deliver a variety of practical sessions – covering everything from making graduate job applications, mock interviews, psychometric testing and group exercises, to

commercial awareness and successful networking. Although most careers services provide their own range of skills training sessions, it's really useful to have employers involved in running these events, especially as they'll often give valuable feedback about what they're looking for during the selection and assessment process.

Having spent time researching the employers that interest you – either through their graduate recruitment website, their brochures and on social media, or meeting them in person at campus events – try to reflect on your particualr skills and experiences and relate them to what employers are asking for, because the next stage is to begin making your applications.

As you go through your university career it's a good idea to keep an accurate record of all your academic results, work experience and other achievements at university. Try to keep all this information together to refer back to when you're filling in individual applications forms, or when tailoring your CV.

Bearing in mind that each application you make is going to take time to prepare and submit, it's important to plan things carefully by making a list of the employers that you're most interested in, along with their application deadlines, to help you prioritise your efforts. Plenty of major

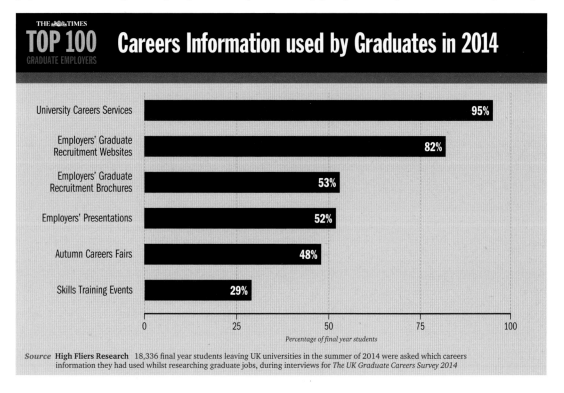

THE TIMES

TOP 100 Careers Information used by Graduates in 2014

GRADUATE EMPLOYERS

Category	Percentage
University Careers Services	95%
Employers' Graduate Recruitment Websites	82%
Employers' Graduate Recruitment Brochures	53%
Employers' Presentations	52%
Autumn Careers Fairs	48%
Skills Training Events	29%

Percentage of final year students

Source **High Fliers Research** 18,336 final year students leaving UK universities in the summer of 2014 were asked which careers information they had used whilst researching graduate jobs, during interviews for *The UK Graduate Careers Survey 2014*

employers have deadlines early in the autumn of your final year, others recruit year-round but on a 'first-come first-served' basis, and some of the smaller recruiters only advertise their vacancies in the summer months.

There is no 'magic number' of applications that will guarantee you a job offer but taking as much care as possible over your applications will help you to be successful. You might not want to put all your eggs in one basket by applying to just one type of employer, but it's equally as important not to take an unfocussed, scattergun approach. Employers want applicants to demonstrate that they really want to work for them.

Remember that the quality of the applications you make will determine whether you're shortlisted for interview. Check carefully for grammatical errors and spelling mistakes in your answers and beware of cutting and pasting between applications – the questions employers ask are often subtly different and you can't simply copy across an answer you've

used on another form, however tempting that may seem. Watch out too for company names – referring to the wrong employer on an application form or in a covering letter is likely to lead you to being rejected.

Many employers now also test their graduate applicants, either as part of the initial online applications or shortly afterwards, on areas such as numeracy and verbal or analytical reasoning. Careers services can sometimes provide practice online tests to help you get used to the format and content of the different exercises. It's important to make use of this because if the first time that you attempt a test is as part of a real application, you're not going to be at your best. It takes practice to know how to time things, how to pace yourself through the test and the type of questions you'll face.

The next stage of the recruitment process is often a first-round interview which could be in person, by telephone, Skype or even via a video interview. Again, preparation is the key to being successful

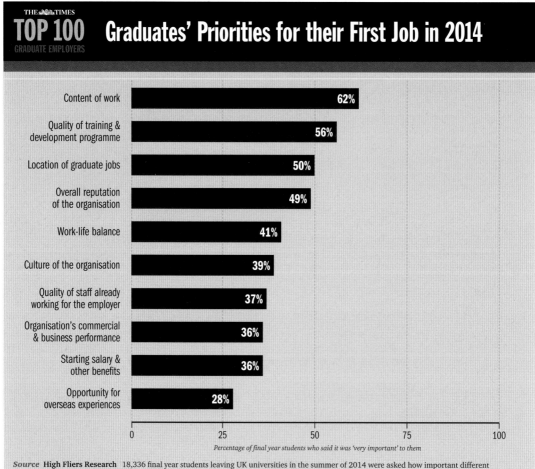

THE TIMES
TOP 100 Graduates' Priorities for their First Job in 2014
GRADUATE EMPLOYERS

Priority	Percentage
Content of work	62%
Quality of training & development programme	56%
Location of graduate jobs	50%
Overall reputation of the organisation	49%
Work-life balance	41%
Culture of the organisation	39%
Quality of staff already working for the employer	37%
Organisation's commercial & business performance	36%
Starting salary & other benefits	36%
Opportunity for overseas experiences	28%

Percentage of final year students who said it was 'very important' to them

Source **High Fliers Research** 18,336 final year students leaving UK universities in the summer of 2014 were asked how important different factors were when deciding which graduate employers to apply to, during interviews for *The UK Graduate Careers Survey 2014*

Five questions to help you decide if law is right for you.

. . . .

Do I have the right kind of brain?
Success in law is not just a question of being clever.
The trainees that do the best with us are inquisitive, logical and commercially minded.

How do I feel about international work?
Many trainees work overseas at some point. Ours are pretty much expected to.

Is it the work that appeals, or the lifestyle?
This is a big one. If the challenge of the work doesn't grab you,
then you'll never really be able to commit to it fully.

Am I ready for some serious reading?
If you can't sit down and get your head around a LOT of paperwork to get to the key issues,
then this may not be for you. It doesn't suit everyone.

Am I comfortable being the one that everyone's looking to for an answer?
You'll eventually find yourself in this position. It happens to our trainees fairly quickly.

. . . .

If you've considered all of these and are still confident that your future lies in law,
then the next question is: where do you apply? We are happy to help with that one too.

nortonrosefulbrightgraduates.com

NORTON ROSE FULBRIGHT

Progress with purpose

here and your careers service may provide practice interviews and help you think through the potential questions or scenarios that an employer might ask you about. Making sure you have thought about your answers to obvious questions such as 'Why do you want this job?' or 'Why do you want to work for us?' will give you much more confidence on the day.

It's also useful to do some broader research into what's going on in the particular sector you've applied to work in. For commercial roles, that could be by reading the business pages of the newspapers or listening to podcasts such as *Wake Up to Money* from BBC Radio Five Live. Being able to demonstrate that you've gone beyond employers' graduate recruitment websites or brochures and are keeping up the latest developments in the industry you're planning to join can make a big difference during an interview.

The final selection round is usually an assessment centre, organised as either a one or sometimes two-day event with a range of different activities designed to test and assess the most promising candidates. This can include group exercises to demonstrate how you work with other people, team or solo presentations, role-play tasks and further one-to-one or group interviews. There could also be an informal lunch or an evening reception which includes the opportunity to talk to managers from the organisation or recent graduates. Be aware of your behaviour in these situations, as you still need to make the best possible impression.

Throughout the assessment centre, the key thing is to participate as fully as possible in each of the exercises – if you don't contribute much to a group

task or challenge, it's very hard for an observer to make any judgements about you.

If at the end of the recruitment process you're in the fortunate position of receiving a job offer, don't feel pressurised into accepting it straight away, particularly if you're waiting to hear the outcome of other applications you've made. If you've got unanswered questions about the role you've been offered, don't be afraid to talk to the graduate recruiters. And if you're lucky enough to have more than one job offer to choose from, it may be useful to talk through your options with a careers adviser before you make your final decision.

For those whose initial applications aren't successful, the main advice is 'don't panic'! It can be very helpful to work with a careers adviser to try and understand where things have gone wrong – is it that you made lots of applications but weren't invited to interview, or did you do several interviews but then didn't progress further? It may be that the sector that you've been applying to isn't quite right for you or there is tough competition. Or it may be that you need more practice at interviews, tests or selection centre exercises.

Remember too that when you do find your first job for after university, it's likely to just be a starting point for your subsequent career and probably won't be something that you'll do for the rest of your working life. Many of the jobs on offer to graduates in the current employment market weren't available at all twenty years ago and careers are continuing to evolve very quickly. In ten or twenty years time today's new graduates could be working in all kinds of roles that haven't even been invented yet.

THE TIMES TOP 100 GRADUATE EMPLOYERS — Job Applications made by Graduates in 2014

	2013		% OF FINALISTS		2013		% OF FINALISTS
1.	1	MARKETING	16.2%	11.	10	ENGINEERING	9.0%
2.	3	CONSULTING	15.8%	12.	11	SALES	8.8%
3.	2	MEDIA	13.3%	13.	12	HUMAN RESOURCES	8.6%
4.	4	TEACHING	12.8%	14.	14	GENERAL MANAGEMENT	6.9%
5.	6	RESEARCH & DEVELOPMENT	12.5%	15.	15	RETAILING	5.8%
6.	5	CHARITY OR VOLUNTARY WORK	12.5%	16.	16	BUYING OR PURCHASING	4.9%
7.	7	INVESTMENT BANKING	11.9%	17.	17	IT	4.3%
8.	8	ACCOUNTANCY	10.8%	18.	19	TRANSPORT OR LOGISTICS	3.1%
9.	13	FINANCE	10.8%	19.	20	ACTUARIAL WORK	2.7%
10.	9	LAW	9.3%	20.	18	ARMED FORCES	2.5%

Source **High Fliers Research** 18,336 final year students leaving UK universities in the summer of 2014 were asked which sectors they had applied to or planned to apply to for graduate jobs, during interviews for *The UK Graduate Careers Survey 2014*

YOU CONTROL A WARSHIP NOT CTRL ALT DELETE

ROYAL NAVY OFFICER

Being an officer in the Royal Navy is a career like any other, but the circumstances and places are sometimes extraordinary. With opportunities ranging from Engineer Officer to Medical Officer, it's a responsible, challenging career that will take you further than you've been before. If you want more than just a job, join the Royal Navy and live a life without limits.

LIFE WITHOUT LIMITS
08456 07 55 55
ROYALNAVY.MOD.UK/CAREERS

Anything but ordinary.

www.lidlgraduatecareers.co.uk

There's nothing ordinary about
our graduate opportunities...

OR OUR GRADUATES!

Graduate Area Management Programme

LOCATIONS NATIONWIDE

Starting on £38k with the potential to earn up to £57,500, plus a
fully expensed Audi A4, private medical cover, company pension
and much more.

We're anything but ordinary! Are you?

If you have what it takes to inspire excellence in one of the most demanding
sectors in the market, take the next step towards the best decision you've
ever made.

Our fast track programme into Area Management is for outstanding, self
motivated individuals, who will make their mark on our business from day one.
The programme offers real responsibility from the moment you join our team,
with a fully supported training programme designed to maximise your potential.
If you're anything but ordinary, we want to know more!

Scan me

To apply online please visit:

www.lidlgraduatecareers.co.uk

Making the Most of Work Experience

By **Greg Hurst**
Education Editor, The Times

Internships and other forms of work experience have become a central feature of the graduate recruitment process. These give undergraduates the opportunity to see at first hand and, sometimes, try out the nature of work in a particular sector and so can help applicants decide if a particular career path suits their talents and personality. More importantly, they enable employers to have a good long look at potential candidates and consider whether they are suited to the organisation.

In theory, both sides benefit. Its effect, however, has been to push the start of the recruitment process forward earlier, forcing students to make career decisions – and to act on them – much sooner during their time at university.

This change, profound as it is, has happened relatively quickly. Until a decade or so ago, most large employers tended to offer work experience placements as a generic benefit to undergraduates as they wended their way through their studies and, usually well into their third year, began to turn their attention to what they might do on graduating.

No longer. Increasingly, internships have become a form of extended courtship between recruiters seeking out the best talent and undergraduates,

much more mindful of the interest ticking up on their larger student loans, scouting for a job with good prospects and worthwhile rewards. Unsurprisingly, therefore, work experience openings with the leading employers have become highly competitive.

For a minority of undergraduates, such opportunities are part of their course or are brokered by their university. Sandwich courses, typically lasting four years with six months or a full year working in industry, are growing in popularity but remain relatively specialist and better suited to degrees such as engineering or vocationally-focused courses like business, marketing, finance and IT.

Most students have to arrange work experience for themselves, although university careers services can help. More employers are offering open days, taster courses and short vacation programmes often in the spring as introductory events for second and, increasingly, first year undergraduates.

Employers' main work experience opportunities are internships over the summer vacation, usually for between six and 12 weeks. Most are paid placements and many employers use similar application and assessment methods to their graduate recruitment programmes. Other forms

> **"** Of the new graduates hired by Top 100 employers in 2014, 37 per cent were recruited through work experience programmes. **"**

WORLD CHANGERS WANTED

VOLUNTARY INTERNSHIP OPPORTUNITIES, UK-WIDE

Ever wanted to change the world? To right wrongs and make a real difference? Take up an internship that takes on poverty, suffering and injustice, and help us change lives worldwide.

Apply now at **www.oxfam.org.uk/getinvolved**

OXFAM

of work experience are also valued by employers, whether they are part-time jobs during the university term, such as bar work or waitressing, or casual work during vacations.

It's clear from the latest annual survey of graduate job hunters just how seriously university students now take work experience. *The UK Graduate Careers Survey*, produced by High Fliers Research and based on face-to-face interviews with 18,336 final year undergraduates at thirty leading universities, found that three-fifths had applied for internships or work placements during university holidays, the highest figure recorded in the twenty years that the survey has been conducted.

Of these, 41 per cent had been offered work experience with a graduate employer. Most found out about such openings via employers' websites, although university careers services were another source of information for many, as was word of mouth from fellow students or recent graduates. A much smaller proportion – one in eight – did a work placement as part of their degree course.

Typically, students said they undertook work experience to boost their chances of getting a graduate job in addition to learning more about an industry or type of work that attracted them. The outcomes were mixed – one in six said that doing so had put them off applying for a job with that employer or working elsewhere in the same sector, while only a third said they were subsequently offered a job by the employer. Not all of them accepted these offers.

Including part-time work during term and holiday jobs, four-fifths of students in their final year of university said they had undertaken some form of work experience whilst at university. The average total duration was six months' experience, the equivalent of two summers' work.

The research makes it clear what a significant difference work experience can have. Analysis of finalists from the 'Class of 2014' who had made job applications shows that those who had done an internship or other work placement were three times more likely to have landed a definite job offer before leaving university, compared with students who'd done no work experience at all.

Feedback from employers also suggests that students are right to take work experience seriously. A survey of senior graduate recruiters at organisations featured in *The Times Top 100 Graduate Employers* found that more than half said they would be unlikely to offer a job to an applicant with no previous experience, irrespective of their degree result or the university they had attended.

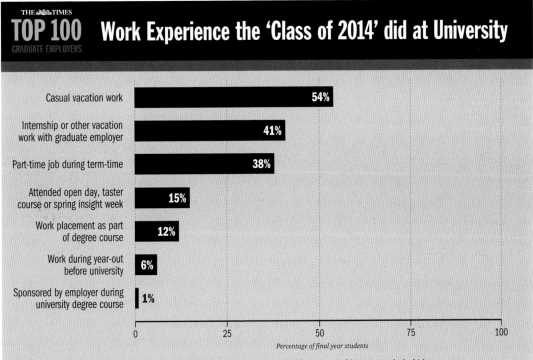

THE TIMES
TOP 100 Work Experience the 'Class of 2014' did at University
GRADUATE EMPLOYERS

Category	Percentage
Casual vacation work	54%
Internship or other vacation work with graduate employer	41%
Part-time job during term-time	38%
Attended open day, taster course or spring insight week	15%
Work placement as part of degree course	12%
Work during year-out before university	6%
Sponsored by employer during university degree course	1%

Percentage of final year students

Source High Fliers Research 18,336 final year students leaving UK universities in the summer of 2014 were asked which types of work experience they had taken part in whilst at time at university, during interviews for *The UK Graduate Careers Survey 2014*

Of the new graduates hired by *Top 100* employers in 2014, 37 per cent were recruited through work experience programmes, compared to 26 per cent in 2010. The major investment banks, which typically pay the highest starting salaries, said they expected to fill 74 per cent of their new graduate positions with people who had already done an internship with them. Consumer goods companies, law firms and other banks & finance companies expected to hire around half of their new graduates through work experience programmes, with oil & gas companies and retailers taking at least a third of their graduates this way.

Some graduate employers target their internships at students studying relevant degrees. Jaguar Land Rover, for example, offers around 140 summer 12-week placements each year, paid at £300 a week, which previously were for engineering students only. This year it also offered a much smaller intake for other business areas such as finance, HR or marketing.

Last year it received around 8,000 applications for these, which were whittled down by online situational judgement tests – in which assessment is automated – psychometric tests and then an assessment day of interviews and group exercises. All are designed to identify candidates with business acumen and persistence who can make decisions rationally and work in teams.

"Just targeting final year students is becoming very, very crowded. A lot of them are snapped up earlier," explains Rob Gill, graduate recruitment manager at Jaguar Land Rover. "Five years ago, if you went to a graduate employers' careers fair at a university, probably 80 or 90 per cent would be final year students looking for jobs for once they graduated. Now it is probably 50:50 of finalists and non-finalists asking about opportunities."

He adds, "We see our undergraduate schemes as a feeder for our graduate schemes. For those going back for their final year after they leave us, we will try and do some sort of assessment of them so they will go back to university knowing whether we intend to offer them some sort of graduate position or not. We are not doing undergraduate placements for benevolent reasons; we are doing it to feed our graduate numbers, so we can get a return on investment."

Other employers take candidates studying a range of courses. Investment banking need not be confined to students studying economics, maths or physics. Steph Ahrens, head of campus recruiting at the investment bank Morgan Stanley, says it seeks to hire talented people with diverse experiences and background, provided they reflect the firm's standards of integrity and excellence.

For analyst roles, Morgan Stanley will consider undergraduates studying a wide variety of disciplines, and look too for examples of leadership, such as involvement in student societies or volunteer work. Technology roles do tend to be targeted at undergraduates studying computer science, engineering, physics or maths.

Morgan Stanley offers a week-long work experience programme over Easter aimed solely at first years, and 10-week paid internships for penultimate-year students, designed to give interns the opportunity to experience the life of a full-time analyst: undergraduates and Masters students work as analysts, and MBAs work at associate level. Industry placements last up to a year.

"The programme begins with a week of classroom training and then interns begin their on-the-job

Work Experience at Top 100 Employers in 2014

THE TIMES — TOP 100 GRADUATE EMPLOYERS

	NUMBER OF PLACEMENTS		NUMBER OF PLACEMENTS
1. INVESTMENT BANKS & FUND MANAGERS	3,189	8. OIL & ENERGY COMPANIES	419
2. ACCOUNTANCY & PROFESSIONAL SERVICES FIRMS	1,844	9. CONSUMER GOODS MANUFACTURERS	375
3. PUBLIC SECTOR EMPLOYERS	1,842	10. RETAILERS	364
4. ENGINEERING & INDUSTRIAL COMPANIES	1,067	11. CHEMICAL & PHARMACEUTICAL COMPANIES	340
5. BANKING & FINANCIAL SERVICES	725	12. CONSULTING FIRMS	174
6. LAW FIRMS	710	13. MEDIA ORGANISATIONS	48
7. IT & TELECOMMUNICATIONS COMPANIES	650	14. TRANSPORT COMPANIES	10

Source High Fliers Research

Make amazing things happen.

Since starting out in 1846 we've been on quite a journey. We've evolved from our traditional telecoms roots into a global communications company.

Our technology connects 68,000 traders through the New York Stock Exchange, linking trading floors in over 60 countries as one virtual trading organisation.

But amazing things don't just happen by themselves. It's about the right people for the job.

Working on challenging projects with ongoing training and an amazing graduate community; there's huge scope for graduates at BT.

Make amazing things happen for your career at **www.btgraduates.com**

experience. Some rotate, some stay in the same group for the duration. They are treated like a full time analyst and therefore get the opportunity to experience the culture and atmosphere of Morgan Stanley and what it is like to work here," says Ms Ahrens.

"These internships and industrial placements are the main pipeline for the full time graduate programmes. If you have enjoyed it and it is something you want to continue with upon graduating and you have impressed us, there is a good chance you will be taken on."

Similarly, about 40 per cent of Deloitte's annual intake of undergraduates are reading science or humanities degrees, alongside those on vocationally-focused courses such as finance or technology. The firm offers a three-day leadership academy for first year students over Easter, with 150 places and ten times as many applicants, and 350 paid summer internships for penultimate year students of three and six weeks, in business areas as diverse as real estate, digital practice, audit, consulting or tax actuarial work.

When selecting for the short taster programmes, candidates are chosen based on broad attributes – the ability to work well in a group, to communicate well with clients, people who are interesting and have something to say, with an analytical mind and the ability to think critically and apply that in their career. The longer work experience placements are, in contrast, highly sector-specific.

"What we want to make sure of is that every candidate who comes on gets a real experience of the work they could potentially be doing as a graduate," says Rob Fryer, head of graduate recruitment at Deloitte. "We are very, very keen to make sure that in the placements they have, they are engaging with clients, they are doing some of the research, they are attending strategy meetings, they are getting a real insight into what it would be like to work as a graduate.

"We work with those people for three to six weeks, so in effect it is an elongated job interview. At the end of their placement, they would have a brief conversation with one of the partners from their group and say 'What did you think? Have you enjoyed it? How did you think you got on?' Probably about 75 per cent of those people would go on to be graduate hires."

Two-thirds of the organisations in *The Times Top 100 Graduate Employers* offer paid internships or similar work placements. Between them, they had 11,819 such places available in 2014 and that number is expected to rise further for 2015.

THE TIMES TOP 100 GRADUATE EMPLOYERS — Work Experience for First Year Students in 2015

EMPLOYER, TYPE OF WORK EXPERIENCE, LENGTH	EMPLOYER, TYPE OF WORK EXPERIENCE, LENGTH
AIRBUS Internships, 3 months	**HSBC** Insight Weeks, 3 days
ARUP Summer Internships, 6-10 weeks	**JAGUAR LAND ROVER** Summer Placements & Internships, 3 months
ATKINS Summer Internships, 12 weeks	**KPMG** First Year Internships, 2 weeks
BANK OF AMERICA MERRILL LYNCH Insight Weeks, 1 week	**L'ORÉAL** Summer Internships, 10 weeks
BARCLAYS Spring Programme, 1 week	**LINKLATERS** Pathfinder, 2 days
BLACKROCK Spring Insight Week, 1 week	**MARS** Summer Internships, 12 weeks
BP IST Discovery Week, 1 week	**MORGAN STANLEY** Insight Programmes, 1 week
CANCER RESEARCH UK Internships, 12 weeks	**NORTON ROSE FULBRIGHT** Open Days, 1-2 days
CITI Spring Programme, 3-5 days	**PENGUIN RANDOM HOUSE** Summer Internships, 10 weeks
CIVIL SERVICE FAST STREAM Early Diversity Internship Programme, 1 week	**PROCTER & GAMBLE** Summer Internships, 10 weeks
CLIFFORD CHANCE Vacation Scheme, 1 week	**PWC** Career Open Days & Talent Academy, 6-8 weeks
CREDIT SUISSE Spring Insight Programme, 1 week	**ROYAL BANK OF SCOTLAND GROUP** Spring Week, 1 week
DELOITTE Spring in Deloitte, 2 days	**SAVILLS** Insight Programme, 1 week
EDF ENERGY Summer Internships, 3 months	**SIEMENS** Summer Internships, 3 months
EY Discover EY, 2 days	**SLAUGHTER AND MAY** Open Day, 1 day
FRESHFIELDS BRUCKHAUS DERINGER Focus Programme, 2 days	**UBS** Spring Insight Week, 1 week
HERBERT SMITH FREEHILLS First Year Workshop, 2 days	**UNILEVER** Spring Programme, 3 days
HOGAN LOVELLS Spring Vacation Scheme, 1 week	

Source **The Times Top 100 Graduate Employers** For full details of these work experience programmes for first year students in 2015 and other opportunities, see employers' individual graduate recruitment websites, as listed on page 240.

The Civil Service Fast Stream – the scheme that recruits candidates with the potential to be future leaders within Whitehall – is one of several public sector employers that is offering work experience in the year ahead. It offers paid summer internships targeted at undergraduates from disadvantaged backgrounds and black and minority ethnic students. From early 2015, it will also introduce spring internships for students from groups under-represented in the Civil Service, at university, schools and colleges.

Phil Wilson, the Fast Stream chief assessor, says, "Former interns are strongly encouraged to apply for permanent positions to build on the experience, understanding and skills they have gained. Fast Stream do not require a specific type of work experience from applicants to the graduate programme, but undoubtedly exposure to our internal internship scheme offers an excellent starting point for evidence provision at final interview stage."

So what about those undergraduates who aren't able to get a place on these highly sought-after placements?

They need not despair, says Rob Fryer at Deloitte. Any form of work experience, however casual or informal, should have benefit, especially when students develop generic skills and can demonstrate an understanding of their role and the business they work in.

"If someone was to work in a bar or clear up litter at Ascot Racecourse, as long as they have developed their skill set, it doesn't matter in what context that is done," he says.

THE TIMES TOP 100 GRADUATE EMPLOYERS
Work Experience for Penultimate Year Students in 2015

EMPLOYER, TYPE OF WORK EXPERIENCE, LENGTH	EMPLOYER, TYPE OF WORK EXPERIENCE, LENGTH
ACCENTURE Summer Vacation Scheme, 8 weeks	**GOOGLE** Internships, 10+ weeks
AIRBUS Internships, 3 months	**GRANT THORNTON** Summer Internships, 4-8 weeks
ARUP Summer Internships, 6-10 weeks	**HERBERT SMITH FREEHILLS** Vacation Schemes, 8 weeks
ATKINS Summer Internships, 12 weeks	**HOGAN LOVELLS** Summer Vacation Scheme, 3 weeks
BAKER & MCKENZIE Summer Vacation Scheme, 3 weeks	**HSBC** Summer Internships, 8-10 weeks
BANK OF AMERICA MERRILL LYNCH Summer Internships, 9 weeks	**IBM** Extreme Blue Summer Internships, 12 weeks
BARCLAYS Summer Internships, 9 weeks	**JAGUAR LAND ROVER** Summer Placements & Internships, 3 months
BLACKROCK Summer Internships, 10 weeks	**KPMG** Vacation Programme, 4, 6 or 8 weeks
BLOOMBERG Summer Internships, 10 weeks	**L'ORÉAL** Summer Internships, 10 weeks
BOOTS Internships, 10 weeks	**LINKLATERS** Vacation Scheme, 3 weeks
BOSTON CONSULTING GROUP Summer Internships, 8 weeks	**LLOYD'S** Summer Internships, 8 weeks
BP Summer Internships, 11 weeks	**MARS** Summer Internships, 12 weeks
CANCER RESEARCH UK Internships, 12 weeks	**MCKINSEY & COMPANY** Summer Internships, 8-12 weeks
CENTRICA Summer Placements, 10 weeks	**MORGAN STANLEY** Summer Analyst Programme, 10 weeks
CITI Summer Internships, 10 weeks	**NORTON ROSE FULBRIGHT** Summer Vacation Scheme, 2 weeks
CIVIL SERVICE FAST STREAM Summer Diversity Internship Programme, 6-9 weeks	**PENGUIN RANDOM HOUSE** Summer Internships, 10 weeks
CLIFFORD CHANCE Vacation Scheme, 2 weeks	**PROCTER & GAMBLE** Summer Internships, 10 weeks
CREDIT SUISSE Summer Analyst Internships, 10 weeks	**PWC** Summer Internships, 6-8 weeks
DELOITTE Summer Vacation Scheme, 3-6 weeks	**ROYAL BANK OF SCOTLAND GROUP** Internships, 10-12 weeks
DLA PIPER Easter & Summer Vacation Work, 2 weeks	**SAINSBURY'S** Summer Internships, 8-10 weeks
DYSON Summer Internships, 3 months	**SAVILLS** Summer Work Experience Scheme, 1 month
EDF ENERGY Summer Internships, 3 months	**SHELL** Internships, 12 weeks
E.ON Summer Placements, c. 12 weeks	**SIEMENS** Summer Internships, 3 months
EXXONMOBIL Summer Internships, 8 weeks	**SLAUGHTER AND MAY** Easter & Summer Work Experience, 1-3 weeks
EY Summer Internships, 6 weeks	**TEACH FIRST** Insight Programme, 2 weeks
FRESHFIELDS BRUCKHAUS DERINGER Summer Vacation Scheme, 3 weeks	**TRANSPORT FOR LONDON** Summer Placements, 12 weeks
FOREIGN & COMMONWEALTH OFFICE Future Talent Internship Scheme, 6 weeks	**UBS** Summer Internships, 9 weeks
GLAXOSMITHKLINE Summer Placements, Up to 12 weeks	**UNILEVER** Summer Placement, 12 weeks

Source **The Times Top 100 Graduate Employers** For full details of these work experience programmes for penultimate year students in 2015 and other opportunities, see employers' individual graduate recruitment websites, as listed on page 240.

TOP 100
GRADUATE EMPLOYERS

The definitive guide to the
recruiting graduates

THE TIMES
TOP 10
GRADUATE EMPLO

The definitive guide to t
recruiting graduates

MES
100
EMPLOYERS

IMES
100
PLOYERS

The definitive guide to the leading employe
recruiting graduates during 2012-2013.

tial guide to the leading employers
duates in 1999-2000.

THE TIMES
TOP 100
ATE EMPLOYERS

THE TIMES
TO
GRADUATE EMI

the leading employe
2006-2007.

THE TIMES
TOP 100

TOP 100 GRADUATE

Fifteen Years of Researching Britain's Top Employers

By **Gill Thomas**
Publisher, *The Times Top 100 Graduate Employers*

It's now fifteen years since the original edition of *The Times Top 100 Graduate Employers* was published, revealing for the first time which organisations the UK's top students aspired to work for after university.

As copies of the first edition were being delivered to campuses around the country in the autumn of 1999, the London Eye was being lifted into place on London's South Bank in readiness for the Millennium celebrations, in the US Bill Clinton was coming to the end of his second term in the White House, the minimum wage was introduced in the UK for the first time, and *Star Wars: The Phantom Menace* became the year's most-watched film at UK cinemas.

Graduates leaving university in 1999 emerged into a particularly buoyant job market. Nationally, unemployment was running at 1.3 million – its lowest level for two decades – and vacancies for graduates had jumped an impressive 12 per cent the previous year, one of the largest annual increases since the late 1980s. Graduate starting salaries were rising quickly too, increasing by nearly twice the annual rate of inflation.

Undergraduates taking part in *The UK Graduate Careers Survey 1999* – the annual survey of final year students' career expectations and aspirations conducted by High Fliers Research – voted

" Thirty-four employers have the dubious record of having only been ranked in the Top 100 once during the last fifteen years. "

Andersen Consulting (then the consulting arm of the accounting firm Arthur Andersen) the year's top graduate employer and more finalists applied for jobs in consulting than any other career area.

Comparing the results of that survey with similar research carried out with the 'Class of 2014' earlier this year shows that in 1999, almost half of the top twenty employers that students believed offered the best opportunities for graduates were manufacturing or industrial companies, whereas just five of the organisations in this year's top twenty actually make anything – the list is dominated instead by retailers, public sector employers and accounting & professional services firms.

A typical salary at a *Top 100* graduate employer this year is £29,500, which is 70 per cent higher than the starting rates for graduates in 1999. The average then was £17,400 and fewer than forty employers offered new recruits packages of £20,000 or more.

Fifteen years ago only 20 per cent of the UK population had access to the internet at home and barely half of finalists went online to research their career options but record numbers took part in employer presentations and university careers fairs. In the 2013-2014 recruitment season, although virtually every graduate job hunter

Ambition is...

making projections for the next blockbuster.

'The training to be an ICAEW Chartered Accountant has provided me with both business skills and integrity, which is extremely valuable in the creative and media sector.'

Chris Hainsworth, ICAEW Chartered Accountant,
Managing Director, AV Pictures

Achieve more as a chartered accountant.

icaew.com/careers

f facebook.com/icaewcareers   🐦 @ICAEW_Careers

ICAEW

relied on employers' websites as a key source of employment information, attendances at campus events such as fairs, presentations and skills training workshops remain as strong as ever.

Andersen Consulting (now Accenture) is one of just three organisations that has made it to number one since *The Times Top 100 Graduate Employers* directory was first published. The firm held onto the top spot for a further three years after 1999 and their success heralded a huge surge in popularity for careers in consulting. At its peak in 2001, almost one in six graduates applied for jobs in the sector. In the year before the firm changed its name from Andersen Consulting to Accenture, it astutely introduced a new graduate package that included a £28,500 starting salary (a sky-high figure for graduates in 2000) and a much talked-about £10,000 bonus, helping to assure the firm's popularity, irrespective of its corporate branding.

In 2003, after two dismal years in graduate recruitment when vacancies for university-leavers dropped by more than a fifth following the terrorist attacks of 11th September 2001, the Civil Service was named Britain's leading graduate employer. Just a year later it was displaced by PricewaterhouseCoopers, the accounting and professional services firm formed from the merger of Price Waterhouse and Coopers & Lybrand in 1998. At the time, the firm was the largest private-sector recruiter of graduates, with an intake in 2004 of more than a thousand trainees.

PricewaterhouseCoopers (now known simply as PwC) has remained at number one for a remarkable eleven years, increasing its share of the student vote from five per cent in 2004 to more than 10 per cent in 2007. The following year, the firm faced its stiffest competition yet from rivals Deloitte and retained the top ranking by just seven votes, but the margin between the firms has increased again and this year more than four hundred votes separated the two employers.

PwC's reign as the leading employer represents a real renaissance for the entire accounting sector. Whereas fifteen years ago, a career in accountancy was regarded as a safe, traditional employment choice, today's profession is viewed in a very different light. The training required to become a chartered accountant is now seen as a prized business qualification and the sector's leading firms are regularly described as 'dynamic' and 'international' by undergraduates looking for their first job after university.

In all, a total of 203 different organisations have now appeared within *The Times Top 100 Graduate Employers* since its inception and over forty of these have made it into the rankings every year for the last fifteen years. The most consistent performers since 1999 have been PwC, KPMG and the Civil Service each of which have never been lower than 8th place in the league table. The NHS has also had a formidable record, appearing in every top ten since 2003, and the BBC, Goldman

---

THE TIMES
TOP 100 **Movers & Shakers in the Top 100**
GRADUATE EMPLOYERS

HIGHEST NEW ENTRIES		HIGHEST CLIMBING EMPLOYERS	
1999	**PFIZER** (31st)	1999	**SCHLUMBERGER** (UP 13 PLACES)
2000	**MORGAN STANLEY** (34th)	2000	**CAPITAL ONE** (UP 32 PLACES)
2001	**MARCONI** (36th)	2001	**EUROPEAN COMMISSION** (UP 36 PLACES)
2002	**GUINNESS UDV** (44th)	2002	**WPP** (UP 36 PLACES)
2003	**ASDA** (40th)	2003	**ROLLS-ROYCE** (UP 37 PLACES)
2004	**BAKER & MCKENZIE** (61st)	2004	**J.P. MORGAN** (UP 29 PLACES)
2005	**PENGUIN** (70th)	2005	**TEACH FIRST** (UP 22 PLACES)
2006	**FUJITSU** (81st)	2006	**GOOGLE** (UP 32 PLACES)
2007	**BDO STOY HAYWARD** (74th)	2007	**PFIZER** (UP 30 PLACES)
2008	**SKY** (76th)	2008	**CO-OPERATIVE GROUP** (UP 39 PLACES)
2009	**BDO STOY HAYWARD** (68th)	2009	**CADBURY** (UP 48 PLACES)
2010	**SAATCHI & SAATCHI** (49th)	2010	**ASDA** (UP 41 PLACES)
2011	**APPLE** (53rd)	2011	**CENTRICA** (UP 41 PLACES)
2012	**EUROPEAN COMMISSION** (56th)	2012	**NESTLÉ** (UP 44 PLACES)
2013	**SIEMENS** (70th)	2013	**DEPARTMENT FOR INTERNATIONAL DEVELOPMENT** (UP 40 PLACES)
2014	**FRONTLINE** (76th)	2014	**TRANSPORT FOR LONDON** (UP 36 PLACES)

Source High Fliers Research

THE TOUGHEST JOB IN THE CITY. COMES WITH THE BIGGEST BONUS.

FRONTLINE

CHANGING LIVES

Frontline is a new initiative designed to recruit outstanding graduates to be leaders in social work and in broader society. Successful applicants will take part in an intensive and innovative two year leadership programme, and gain a masters degree. But most importantly, they'll be working to transform the lives of vulnerable children and young people.

Because there's no bigger bonus than changing a life for the better.

www.thefrontline.org.uk

Sachs and EY (formerly Ernst & Young) have all remained within the top twenty throughout the last decade.

Google and Jaguar Land Rover have climbed the furthest within the *Top 100*, both jumping more than seventy places up the rankings in the last decade. Other employers haven't been so successful though – British Airways, ranked in 6th place in 1999, dropped out of the *Top 100* altogether in 2010 and Ford, which was once rated as high as 14th, disappeared out of the list in 2006 after cancelling its graduate recruitment programme two years previously.

Thirty four employers – including Nokia, Maersk, the Home Office, Cable & Wireless, United Biscuits, Nationwide, Capgemini and the Met Office – have the dubious record of having only been ranked in the *Top 100* once during the last fifteen years.

And Marconi had the unusual distinction of being one of the highest-ever new entries in 36th place in 2001, only to vanish from the list entirely the following year.

One of the most spectacular ascendancies within the *Top 100* has been the rise of Aldi which joined the list in 65th place in 2002 and rose to 3rd place in 2009, helped in part by its memorable remuneration package for new recruits (currently £41,000 plus an Audi A4 car), and is again ranked within the top five in 2014.

Teach First, however, continues to be the most impressive new entrant since the launch of the *Top 100* in 1999. After first appearing in 63rd place in 2003, the scheme has now reached 2nd place and is set to be the UK's largest individual recruiter of graduates in 2015, with an unprecedented 2,060 places available on its two-year programme.

THE TIMES TOP 100 GRADUATE EMPLOYERS — Winners & Losers in the Top 100

MOST CONSISTENT EMPLOYERS 1999-2014

	HIGHEST RANKING	LOWEST RANKING
ANDERSEN (FORMERLY ARTHUR ANDERSEN)	**2nd** (1999-2001)	**3rd** (2002)
PWC	**1st** (2004-2014)	**3rd** (1999-2001, 2003)
KPMG	**3rd** (2006-2008, 2011-2012)	**8th** (1999)
CIVIL SERVICE	**1st** (2003)	**8th** (2011)
BBC	**5th** (2005-2007)	**14th** (1999)
GLAXOSMITHKLINE	**11th** (2000)	**22nd** (2002-2003)
IBM	**13th** (2000)	**24th** (2012)
EY (FORMERLY ERNST & YOUNG)	**7th** (2013)	**20th** (2001)
BP	**14th** (2013-2014)	**32nd** (2004)
ACCENTURE (FORMERLY ANDERSEN CONSULTING)	**1st** (1999-2002)	**20th** (2014)

EMPLOYERS CLIMBING HIGHEST 1999-2014

	NEW ENTRY RANKING	HIGHEST RANKING
GOOGLE	**85th** (2005)	**9th** (2014)
JAGUAR LAND ROVER	**87th** (2009)	**16th** (2014)
MI5 – THE SECURITY SERVICE	**96th** (2007)	**33rd** (2010)
ALDI	**65th** (2002)	**3rd** (2009)
TEACH FIRST	**63rd** (2004)	**2nd** (2014)
LIDL	**89th** (2009)	**31st** (2013)
ATKINS	**94th** (2004)	**37th** (2009)
ARCADIA GROUP	**99th** (2001)	**47th** (2007)
SLAUGHTER AND MAY	**90th** (2001)	**39th** (2010)
NESTLÉ	**93rd** (2009)	**43rd** (2013)

EMPLOYERS FALLING FURTHEST 1999-2014

	HIGHEST RANKING	LOWEST RANKING
BRITISH AIRWAYS	**6th** (1999)	**Not ranked** (2010, 2011)
FORD	**11th** (1999)	**Not ranked** (FROM 2006)
THOMPSON REUTERS	**22nd** (2001)	**Not ranked** (2009-2012)
ASTRAZENECA	**24th** (2003)	**Not ranked** (FROM 2012)
MINISTRY OF DEFENCE	**35th** (2003)	**Not ranked** (2007, FROM 2012)
MARCONI	**36th** (2001)	**Not ranked** (FROM 2002)
DIAGEO	**37th** (2004)	**Not ranked** (2008-2009)
ICI	**39th** (2000)	**Not ranked** (2001, 2004, FROM 2006)
LOGICA	**39th** (1999)	**Not ranked** (FROM 2003)
QINETIQ	**43rd** (2001)	**Not ranked** (2007, FROM 2011)

Source High Fliers Research

THE TIMES

TOP 100
GRADUATE EMPLOYERS

The Top 10 Graduate Employers 1999-2013

1999
1. ANDERSEN CONSULTING
2. ARTHUR ANDERSEN
3. PRICEWATERHOUSECOOPERS
4. PROCTER & GAMBLE
5. GOLDMAN SACHS
6. CIVIL SERVICE
7. KPMG
8. UNILEVER
9. ARMY
10. MARS

2000
1. ANDERSEN CONSULTING
2. PRICEWATERHOUSECOOPERS
3. ARTHUR ANDERSEN
4. CIVIL SERVICE
5. ARMY
6. KPMG
7. UNILEVER
8. PROCTER & GAMBLE
9. GOLDMAN SACHS
10. MARS

2001
1. ACCENTURE (FORMERLY ANDERSEN CONSULTING)
2. ANDERSEN (FORMERLY ARTHUR ANDERSEN)
3. PRICEWATERHOUSECOOPERS
4. PROCTER & GAMBLE
5. GOLDMAN SACHS
6. CIVIL SERVICE
7. KPMG
8. UNILEVER
9. ARMY
10. MARS

2002
1. ACCENTURE
2. PRICEWATERHOUSECOOPERS
3. ANDERSEN
4. CIVIL SERVICE
5. ARMY
6. KPMG
7. UNILEVER
8. PROCTER & GAMBLE
9. GOLDMAN SACHS
10. MARS

2003
1. CIVIL SERVICE
2. ACCENTURE
3. PRICEWATERHOUSECOOPERS
4. ARMY
5. KPMG
6. HSBC
7. BBC
8. PROCTER & GAMBLE
9. NHS
10. DELOITTE & TOUCHE

2004
1. PRICEWATERHOUSECOOPERS
2. CIVIL SERVICE
3. ACCENTURE
4. KPMG
5. NHS
6. BBC
7. ARMY
8. PROCTER & GAMBLE
9. HSBC
10. DELOITTE (FORMERLY DELOITTE & TOUCHE)

2005
1. PRICEWATERHOUSECOOPERS
2. CIVIL SERVICE
3. ACCENTURE
4. KPMG
5. BBC
6. DELOITTE
7. NHS
8. HSBC
9. GOLDMAN SACHS
10. PROCTER & GAMBLE

2006
1. PRICEWATERHOUSECOOPERS
2. DELOITTE
3. KPMG
4. CIVIL SERVICE
5. BBC
6. NHS
7. HSBC
8. ACCENTURE
9. PROCTER & GAMBLE
10. GOLDMAN SACHS

2007
1. PRICEWATERHOUSECOOPERS
2. DELOITTE
3. KPMG
4. CIVIL SERVICE
5. BBC
6. NHS
7. ACCENTURE
8. HSBC
9. ALDI
10. GOLDMAN SACHS

2008
1. PRICEWATERHOUSECOOPERS
2. DELOITTE
3. KPMG
4. ACCENTURE
5. NHS
6. CIVIL SERVICE
7. BBC
8. ALDI
9. TEACH FIRST
10. GOLDMAN SACHS

2009
1. PRICEWATERHOUSECOOPERS
2. DELOITTE
3. ALDI
4. CIVIL SERVICE
5. KPMG
6. NHS
7. ACCENTURE
8. TEACH FIRST
9. BBC
10. ERNST & YOUNG

2010
1. PRICEWATERHOUSECOOPERS
2. DELOITTE
3. CIVIL SERVICE
4. KPMG
5. ALDI
6. NHS
7. TEACH FIRST
8. ACCENTURE
9. BBC
10. ERNST & YOUNG

2011
1. PWC (FORMERLY PRICEWATERHOUSECOOPERS)
2. DELOITTE
3. KPMG
4. ALDI
5. NHS
6. BBC
7. TEACH FIRST
8. CIVIL SERVICE
9. ACCENTURE
10. ERNST & YOUNG

2012
1. PWC
2. DELOITTE
3. KPMG
4. TEACH FIRST
5. ALDI
6. NHS
7. CIVIL SERVICE
8. ERNST & YOUNG
9. BBC
10. JOHN LEWIS PARTNERSHIP

2013
1. PWC
2. DELOITTE
3. TEACH FIRST
4. KPMG
5. CIVIL SERVICE
6. ALDI
7. EY (FORMERLY ERNST & YOUNG)
8. NHS
9. JOHN LEWIS PARTNERSHIP
10. GOOGLE

Source High Fliers Research

TeachFirst

"I wanted to make a difference, so I did"

Robin Hartfield Cross Taught: **Maths**
Now: **PwC Graduate Scheme**

20% of pupils eligible for free school meals
make it to university, compared to 86% from
independent schools.

**Change their lives.
Change yours.**

Apply now for our Leadership Development Programme   teachfirst.org.uk

ONLY
£20
A YEAR

THE TIMES
THE SUNDAY TIMES

FOR STUDENTS OF TODAY
AND CEOs OF TOMORROW

The Student Membership.

News, sport and exclusive member
rewards from Times+. On the web and
your smartphone. Only £20 a year.

thetimes.co.uk/studentmembership

Full Ts & Cs apply

THE TIMES
TOP 100
GRADUATE EMPLOYERS

	PAGE		PAGE		PAGE
Accenture	60	E.ON	122	Metropolitan Police	180
Airbus	62	EDF Energy	124	MI5 – The Security Service	182
Aldi	64	European		Microsoft	184
Allen & Overy	66	Commission (EU Careers)	126	Mondelēz International	186
Arcadia Group	68	ExxonMobil	128	Morgan Stanley	188
Army	70	EY	130	Morrisons	190
Arup	72	Foreign &		Newton Europe	192
Asda	74	Commonwealth Office	132	NGDP for	
Atkins	76	Freshfields Bruckhaus		Local Government	194
Baker & McKenzie	78	Deringer	134	NHS	196
Bank of America		Frontline	136	Norton Rose Fulbright	198
Merrill Lynch	80	GlaxoSmithKline	138	Oxfam	200
Barclays	82	Goldman Sachs	140	Penguin Random House	202
BBC	84	Google	142	Procter & Gamble	204
BlackRock	86	Grant Thornton	144	PwC	206
Bloomberg	88	Herbert Smith Freehills	146	Rolls-Royce	208
Boots	90	Hogan Lovells	148	Royal Air Force	210
Boston Consulting Group	92	HSBC	150	Royal Bank of	
BP	94	IBM	152	Scotland Group	212
British Airways	96	Jaguar Land Rover	154	Royal Navy	214
British Sugar	98	John Lewis Partnership	156	Sainsbury's	216
BT	100	J.P.Morgan	158	Savills	218
Cancer Research UK	102	KPMG	160	Shell	220
Centrica	104	L'Oréal	162	Siemens	222
Citi	106	Lidl	164	Sky	224
Civil Service Fast Stream	108	Linklaters	166	Slaughter and May	226
Clifford Chance	110	Lloyd's	168	Teach First	228
Credit Suisse	112	Lloyds Banking Group	170	Tesco	230
Deloitte	114	Marks & Spencer	172	Transport for London	232
Diageo	116	Mars	174	UBS	234
DLA Piper	118	McDonald's	176	Unilever	236
Dyson	120	McKinsey & Company	178	WPP	238

EMPLOYER	TOP 100 RANKING	Accountancy	Consulting	Engineering	Finance	General Management	Human Resources	Investment Banking	IT	Law	Logistics	Marketing	Media	Property	Purchasing	Research & Development	Retailing	Sales	NUMBER OF VACANCIES	PAGE
ACCENTURE	20		●						●										350-400	60
AIRBUS	55			●	●	●			●					●	●				50-60	62
ALDI	4				●												●		175	64
ALLEN & OVERY	35									●									85	66
ARCADIA GROUP	79				●												●		200+	68
ARMY	28				●				●	●	●								650	70
ARUP	27	●	●	●	●														200+	72
ASDA	60				●							●		●			●		20-30	74
ATKINS	49	●	●	●	●								●						300	76
BAKER & McKENZIE	67									●									30	78
BANK OF AMERICA MERRILL LYNCH	65				●			●	●										200	80
BARCLAYS	13	●			●	●	●	●	●			●							200+	82
BBC	8		●						●				●	●					50+	84
BLACKROCK	61	●			●				●			●					●		90-100	86
BLOOMBERG	86				●				●								●		300+	88
BOOTS	88	●			●	●			●		●	●		●		●			60	90
BOSTON CONSULTING GROUP	44		●																No fixed quota	92
BP	14	●		●	●	●	●	●	●		●			●	●	●	●		150	94
BRITISH AIRWAYS	45	●	●	●	●				●					●	●				75+	96
BRITISH SUGAR	77	●		●	●	●				●							●		No fixed quota	98
BT	43		●	●	●				●	●		●		●			●		200	100
CANCER RESEARCH UK	56			●	●	●			●			●		●					8	102
CENTRICA	75			●	●	●	●		●			●							60+	104
CITI	47					●		●	●										180-220	106
CIVIL SERVICE FAST STREAM	6			●	●	●	●		●			●		●					800+	108
CLIFFORD CHANCE	32									●									100	110
CREDIT SUISSE	57				●			●	●								●		150+	112
DELOITTE	3	●	●		●				●				●						1,200	114
DIAGEO	97			●	●	●						●					●		50	116
DLA PIPER	90									●									80	118
DYSON	94	●		●								●		●					70+	120
E.ON	95			●	●	●	●		●								●		45-50	122
EDF ENERGY	93			●	●	●	●												Around 60	124
EUROPEAN COMMISSION (EU CAREERS)	70			●	●	●			●	●		●	●		●				No fixed quota	126
EXXONMOBIL	72			●	●	●			●			●							No fixed quota	128
EY	11	●	●		●				●										800	130
FOREIGN & COMMONWEALTH OFFICE	51				●	●	●				●		●		●				Around 35	132
FRESHFIELDS BRUCKHAUS DERINGER	40									●									80	134
FRONTLINE	76					●	●		●						●				132	136
GLAXOSMITHKLINE	15			●	●	●			●			●		●	●	●			65+	138
GOLDMAN SACHS	17	●			●			●	●										300	140
GOOGLE	9		●	●		●			●				●	●					No fixed quota	142
GRANT THORNTON	62	●																	300+	144
HERBERT SMITH FREEHILLS	84									●									70	146
HOGAN LOVELLS	83									●									60	148

EMPLOYER	TOP 100 RANKING	ACCOUNTANCY	CONSULTING	ENGINEERING	FINANCE	GENERAL MANAGEMENT	HUMAN RESOURCES	INVESTMENT BANKING	IT	LAW	LOGISTICS	MARKETING	MEDIA	PROPERTY	PURCHASING	RESEARCH & DEVELOPMENT	RETAILING	SALES	NUMBER OF VACANCIES	PAGE
HSBC	21				●			●										●	300+	150
IBM	22		●						●									●	300+	152
JAGUAR LAND ROVER	16			●	●		●		●		●	●		●	●	●			270	154
JOHN LEWIS PARTNERSHIP	10			●	●			●						●		●			79	156
J.P. MORGAN	18	●		●		●	●	●							●				No fixed quota	158
KPMG	7	●	●		●		●		●										1,000	160
L'ORÉAL	41			●							●	●						●	40	162
LIDL	31				●							●	●			●	●		100	164
LINKLATERS	34									●									110	166
LLOYD'S	85				●														12-15	168
LLOYDS BANKING GROUP	30		●		●	●	●	●	●			●							400	170
MARKS & SPENCER	33			●	●		●			●	●			●	●	●			200	172
MARS	48			●	●	●					●			●	●			●	35	174
MCDONALD'S	59				●												●		250-350	176
MCKINSEY & COMPANY	29		●																No fixed quota	178
METROPOLITAN POLICE	73																		To be confirmed	180
MI5	52				●				●										80+	182
MICROSOFT	24		●						●									●	36	184
MONDELĒZ INTERNATIONAL	91		●	●		●					●	●			●			●	Around 40	186
MORGAN STANLEY	37			●		●	●	●											No fixed quota	188
MORRISONS	100			●	●	●		●		●	●			●			●		100+	190
NEWTON EUROPE	98		●						●										50	192
NGDP	53				●														100-120	194
NHS	5			●	●	●		●											To be confirmed	196
NORTON ROSE FULBRIGHT	87									●									Up to 55	198
OXFAM	78	●			●		●				●	●			●	●			50+ (voluntary)	200
PENGUIN RANDOM HOUSE	82	●		●		●				●	●	●							50+	202
PROCTER & GAMBLE	26		●	●	●		●			●	●			●				●	100	204
PWC	1	●	●		●				●	●									1,200	206
ROLLS-ROYCE	19		●	●	●	●								●				●	Around 400	208
ROYAL AIR FORCE	74			●		●	●		●	●									No fixed quota	210
ROYAL BANK OF SCOTLAND GROUP	36	●			●	●	●	●	●			●							350+	212
ROYAL NAVY	68			●	●	●			●		●				●				No fixed quota	214
SAINSBURY'S	39				●	●			●		●	●		●	●	●	●		36	216
SAVILLS	89													●					70+	218
SHELL	25			●	●		●		●		●	●				●			150-200	220
SIEMENS	66			●	●	●								●			●		80+	222
SKY	54	●	●		●	●	●		●			●	●	●				●	90+	224
SLAUGHTER AND MAY	58									●									75-80	226
TEACH FIRST	2	●	●	●	●	●	●	●	●	●	●	●	●	●	●	●	●	●	2,060	228
TESCO	23			●	●	●		●		●	●		●	●	●		●		100+	230
TRANSPORT FOR LONDON	63	●			●	●	●		●			●							130	232
UBS	81							●											100+	234
UNILEVER	12			●	●		●				●	●			●			●	50	236
WPP	38										●	●							1-10	238

EMPLOYER   TOP 100 RANKING   GRADUATE VACANCIES IN 2015   NUMBER OF VACANCIES   PAGE

EVOLVE YOURSELF

accenture.com/top100

Accenture is a world-leading provider of strategy, digital, technology and operations expertise that's transforming the way many of the biggest organisations approach business. It's also the perfect choice for a consulting career that will inspire as it challenges.

With the launch this year of two new business areas – Accenture Strategy and Accenture Digital – working alongside Accenture Technology and Accenture Operations, the business continues to bring world-class skills, consulting capabilities and integrated solutions that really work. It's not just clients that benefit – graduates who choose Accenture can benefit greatly too, evolving their skills, working with a broad range of clients and contributing to projects that are revolutionising whole industries. From re-engineering working environments for greater efficiency with smartwatch technology to enhancing engineering expertise with augmented reality apps, Accenture's consultative work forms the ideal bedrock for graduates to begin building a career as stimulating as it is rewarding.

Graduates who choose a consulting career will be part of either Accenture Digital, Technology Consulting, Accenture Strategy or will join within one of the industry groups. Industry groups include Communications, Media & Technology, Financial Services, Health & Public Service, Products and Resources. Alternatively, graduates can take the path that allows them to hone their talents for Software Engineering, working in the Client Delivery & Operations part of the business.

For Consulting, a 2:1 in any discipline is required and for Software Engineering, applicants need a 2:1 in a technology, maths, science or engineering-related degree. Both require a genuine passion for technology.

GRADUATE VACANCIES IN 2015

CONSULTING

IT

NUMBER OF VACANCIES
350-400 graduate jobs

LOCATIONS OF VACANCIES

STARTING SALARY FOR 2015
Up to £31,500
Plus a £10,000 sign-on bonus for Consulting roles.

UNIVERSITY VISITS IN 2014-15
ASTON, BATH, BRISTOL, BRUNEL, CAMBRIDGE, DURHAM, EDINBURGH, EXETER, IMPERIAL COLLEGE LONDON, KING'S COLLEGE LONDON, KENT, LEEDS, LONDON SCHOOL OF ECONOMICS, LOUGHBOROUGH, MANCHESTER, NEWCASTLE, NOTTINGHAM, OXFORD, SOUTHAMPTON, ST ANDREWS, SURREY, UNIVERSITY COLLEGE LONDON, WARWICK
Please check with your university careers service for full details of local events.

MINIMUM ENTRY REQUIREMENTS
2.1 Degree

APPLICATION DEADLINE
Year-round recruitment
Early application advised.

FURTHER INFORMATION
www.Top100GraduateEmployers.com
Register now for the latest news, events information and graduate recruitment details for Britain's leading employers.

be > you imagined

Be greater than.

Bring your talent and passion to a global organisation at the forefront of business, technology and innovation. Collaborate with diverse, talented colleagues and leaders who support your success. Help transform organisations and communities around the world. Sharpen your skills through industry leading training and development, as you build an extraordinary career. Discover how great you can be. Visit accenture.com/ukgraduates

Strategy | Digital | Technology | Operations

> **accenture**
High performance. Delivered.

AIRBUS GROUP

The Airbus Group is a global pioneer in aeronautics, space and defence-related services. Combining European heritage with global outreach, the company develops an array of products, including the world's largest commercial aircraft – the double-deck Airbus A380, the newly awakened comet explorer – Rosetta, and the record-breaking helicopter – the X3.

Airbus is the leading commercial aircraft manufacturer, offering the most cutting-edge family of airliners on the market. It has played a key role in the evolution of international air transport over the last 40 years and today captures about half of all commercial airliner orders.

Airbus Defence and Space (formerly Astrium, Airbus Military and Cassidian) is number one in defence and the second largest space business in the world. Creating innovative solutions in defence and space, the division drives the industry forward and its technology connects and protects lives.

For people with ingenuity, commercial awareness and exceptional problem-solving skills, the Airbus UK Graduate Programme and the Airbus Defence and Space UK Graduate Programme both offer a rare opportunity to help shape and develop the innovative products of the future.

The programmes consist of structured rotational placements, which offer exposure to a broad range of business functions and allow graduates to expand their technical and management competencies. Personal development strategies and training courses help them plan their future careers. In addition, they can take part in education and community projects to broaden their individual skills.

In either division, graduates will have the chance to challenge perspectives – of colleagues, customers and the industry at large – and will be encouraged to explore new ideas, think innovatively and deliver solutions that go beyond the norm.

GRADUATE VACANCIES IN 2015
ENGINEERING
FINANCE
HUMAN RESOURCES
IT
LOGISTICS
PURCHASING
RESEARCH & DEVELOPMENT

NUMBER OF VACANCIES
50-60 graduate jobs

LOCATIONS OF VACANCIES

STARTING SALARY FOR 2015
£26,000
Plus a welcome payment for graduates.

UNIVERSITY VISITS IN 2014-15
BATH, BIRMINGHAM, BRISTOL, CAMBRIDGE, IMPERIAL COLLEGE LONDON, LEICESTER, LIVERPOOL, LOUGHBOROUGH, MANCHESTER, SHEFFIELD, SOUTHAMPTON, SURREY, UNIVERSITY COLLEGE LONDON
Please check with your university careers service for full details of local events.

MINIMUM ENTRY REQUIREMENTS
2.2 Degree

APPLICATION DEADLINE
28th November 2014
31st December 2014 for Airbus Defence and Space.

FURTHER INFORMATION
www.Top100GraduateEmployers.com
Register now for the latest news, events information and graduate recruitment details for Britain's leading employers.

CHALLENGING PERSPECTIVES

A world of opportunities for your career

Ready to turn conventional wisdom on its head?

Join the Airbus Group, a global pioneer in aeronautics, space and defence-related services on one of our two UK Graduate Programmes and you'll have the opportunity to work on technological innovations that change the way our customers see the world.

The **Airbus UK Graduate Programme** is an exceptional two/three-year training programme with support for professional accreditation. Graduates are trained in business management and cultural awareness, personal effectiveness and technical understanding.

The **Airbus Defence and Space UK Graduate Programme** is two years in duration and provides outstanding development as well as an introduction to several areas of the business offering an opportunity to gain real hands on experience.

No matter which division you join, you can ensure that the Airbus Group offers a unique environment and great prospects – an ideal place to start your career.

Find out more at **www.jobs.airbus-group.com**

GRADUATE VACANCIES IN 2015
GENERAL MANAGEMENT
RETAILING

NUMBER OF VACANCIES
175 graduate jobs

LOCATIONS OF VACANCIES

Aldi is renowned for attracting top quality, ambitious graduates who have a determination to succeed, for its Area Management Programme. In addition to a market-leading remuneration package of £41,000 rising to £67,750 after four years, Aldi offers graduates real responsibility from day one.

Graduates who possess an ability to inspire, lead and motivate a growing retail team within a fast-paced environment are highly sought after, as these qualities have made Aldi a driving force in the UK's retail landscape.

Aldi Area Managers must be team players – the business actively seeks out graduates who can demonstrate leadership qualities, either through academic or extra-curricular activities. The initiative and skills required to lead a local or university team, undertake voluntary work, or strive for personal excellence are highly valued. Aldi is looking for self-starters who can lead and motivate large store teams within one of the UK's fastest growing companies.

Candidates who are selected for Aldi's Area Management Programme begin their journey in-store and within weeks will be managing a store of their own. Maintaining high standards and attention to detail are expected throughout the role and in return, Aldi offers fast-track career progression and real responsibility.

After receiving comprehensive training in all aspects of retail management, from store operations through to financial administration, Aldi graduate trainees are given the skills to take charge of a multi-million pound area of three to four stores to run, as and when they are ready.

To be successful, graduates will need good academics, high energy levels, a willingness to learn and the determination to overcome the challenges ahead. In return, Aldi offers an excellent starting salary and a fully expensed Audi A4.

STARTING SALARY FOR 2015
£41,000

UNIVERSITY VISITS IN 2014-15
ABERDEEN, ASTON, BATH, BIRMINGHAM, CARDIFF, DUNDEE, DURHAM, EAST ANGLIA, EDINBURGH, EXETER, GLASGOW, LANCASTER, LEEDS, LEICESTER, LIVERPOOL, LONDON SCHOOL OF ECONOMICS, LOUGHBOROUGH, MANCHESTER, NEWCASTLE, NORTHUMBRIA, NOTTINGHAM, SHEFFIELD, SOUTHAMPTON, ST ANDREWS, STRATHCLYDE, WARWICK, YORK
Please check with your university careers service for full details of local events.

MINIMUM ENTRY REQUIREMENTS
2.1 Degree

APPLICATION DEADLINE
Year-round recruitment

FURTHER INFORMATION
www.Top100GraduateEmployers.com
Register now for the latest news, events information and graduate recruitment details for Britain's leading employers.

If you didn't love this job, you couldn't do it. It's not just about the money.

Graduate Area Manager Programme

I won't lie, it can be really, really tough working at Aldi. The graduate programme is hard and there's an awful lot of training. But you're faced with the most incredible challenges and that's what I love being part of. This is the UK's fastest-growing supermarket, and we're all driving productivity and efficiency. I love the clarity of it all: it's a meritocracy. Your progression is based on how good you want to be. Everything just works. It feels great and I like it.

aldirecruitment.co.uk/graduates

LIKE NO OTHER

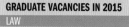
ALLEN & OVERY

Allen & Overy is a pioneering legal practice operating around the world at the frontline of developing business. By helping companies, institutions and governments tackle ever more complex issues and transactions on a global stage, it is leading the way and extending what is possible in law.

With 44 offices in 30 countries, plus a network of relationship firms in other locations, Allen & Overy is one of the few legal practices that can genuinely claim to be global, covering 99% of the world's economy.

For the firm's clients this means global reach and access to high-calibre, local expertise, while for trainees, it means exposure to international work, collaboration with colleagues in other offices and, in many cases, the opportunity to travel. In 2013, 26% of its transactional work involved five or more countries.

Trainee lawyers joining the firm enter an environment characterised by advanced thinking and a global outlook. They are exposed to challenging and meaningful work from the outset, supporting a partner or senior associate in each of their training 'seats'. In addition, they are encouraged to spend six months in one of the firm's overseas offices, or on secondment to one of its corporate clients – currently around 80% of its trainees take up this opportunity.

Alongside a rich and exciting experience as a trainee, graduates can also look forward to working in a uniquely open and supportive culture. Allen & Overy has established a reputation for combining the very highest professional standards with warmth and approachability.

Regardless of their degree discipline – and around half of the firm's trainees study subjects other than law – joining Allen & Overy puts graduates at the forefront of the rapidly-evolving global market for legal services.

GRADUATE VACANCIES IN 2015
LAW

NUMBER OF VACANCIES
85 graduate jobs
For training contracts starting in 2017.

LOCATIONS OF VACANCIES

STARTING SALARY FOR 2015
£39,000

UNIVERSITY VISITS IN 2014-15
BATH, BELFAST, BIRMINGHAM, BRISTOL, CAMBRIDGE, CARDIFF, DURHAM, EDINBURGH, EXETER, IMPERIAL COLLEGE LONDON, KING'S COLLEGE LONDON, LANCASTER, LEEDS, LEICESTER, LONDON SCHOOL OF ECONOMICS, MANCHESTER, NEWCASTLE, NOTTINGHAM, OXFORD, SCHOOL OF AFRICAN STUDIES, SHEFFIELD, SOUTHAMPTON, ST ANDREWS, TRINITY COLLEGE DUBLIN, UNIVERSITY COLLEGE DUBLIN, UNIVERSITY COLLEGE LONDON, WARWICK, YORK
Please check with your university careers service for full details of local events.

MINIMUM ENTRY REQUIREMENTS
2.1 Degree
340 UCAS points

APPLICATION DEADLINE
Law: 31st July 2015
Non-law: 31st December 2014

FURTHER INFORMATION
www.Top100GraduateEmployers.com
Register now for the latest news, events information and graduate recruitment details for Britain's leading employers.

ALLEN & OVERY

A CAREER IN LAW

Setting precedents, not following them…
because tomorrow will not be like today.

Being a lawyer at Allen & Overy means having the vision to think beyond what has been done before and the courage to move first. We have pioneered the introduction of part-time partnerships to diversify our leadership and taken a lead in broadening access to the professions and addressing social mobility through PRIME. We were also the first major international firm to build a presence in new frontiers such as Australia, Dubai and Morocco, recognising the gravitational shift of business to new markets.

Joining us you will learn to live on the front foot, always evolving, always advancing and always looking for new opportunities and new ways to improve the services we deliver.

Find out more at **www.aograduate.com**

Follow the conversation **@AllenOveryGrads** | **www.facebook.com/allenoverygrads**

Arcadia

GRADUATE VACANCIES IN 2015

FINANCE

RETAILING

NUMBER OF VACANCIES
200+ graduate jobs

LOCATIONS OF VACANCIES

Arcadia is a business like no other. It's the UK's largest privately owned fashion retailer, with eight major high street brands: BHS, Burton, Dorothy Perkins, Evans, Miss Selfridge, Topshop, Topman and Wallis, along with the out-of-town fashion destination Outfit.

It's not just about the UK high street; with online stores and over 550 global locations, Arcadia's presence is felt all over the world. From factories to deliveries, employees to suppliers, every part of the business has a footprint. Whether it's working to improve the welfare of its overseas factory workers or reducing the number of lorries on the road, Arcadia is constantly looking for ways to be safer, friendly and more sustainable.

It takes exceptional people to keep so many different brands at the forefront of a rapidly changing industry and Arcadia's people demonstrate a perfect combination of strong commercial skills and real passion for the business. It's not only Arcadia's products but its people who drive the success of the business. Arcadia's graduate recruits are no exception to this. Whichever cornerstone of the business – Buying, Digital, Finance or Merchandising – graduates can count on tailored on-the-job training and a manager who really understands the importance of giving responsibility from day one.

Arcadia recruit for Buying, Digital and Merchandising all year round, whilst the Finance programme is recruited three times a year. After the initial application, graduates will be invited to a video interview and those who are successful will then participate in a face-to-face assessment where brand/department fit is identified.

Alongside a competitive salary, great benefits including 25% discount, Arcadia offers bespoke training and development at all levels with career paths to match.

STARTING SALARY FOR 2015
£19,000-£24,000

UNIVERSITY VISITS IN 2014-15
LEEDS, MANCHESTER, NOTTINGHAM, NOTTINGHAM TRENT, SHEFFIELD
Please check with your university careers service for full details of local events.

MINIMUM ENTRY REQUIREMENTS
2.2 Degree
Relevant degree required for some roles.

APPLICATION DEADLINE
Year-round recruitment

FURTHER INFORMATION
www.Top100GraduateEmployers.com
Register now for the latest news, events information and graduate recruitment details for Britain's leading employers.

Arcadia

BUYING

DIGITAL

FINANCE

MERCHANDISING

www.arcadiagroup.co.uk/careers

ARMY
BE THE BEST

army.mod.uk/officer

twitter.com/armyjobs 🐦 facebook.com/armyofficerjobs f

youtube.com/armyjobs ▶ linkedin.com/company/british-army in

Life for Officers in the British Army is far from routine. They believe there's no other job that offers the same level of challenge, reward, excitement and adventure. Right from the start, Officers will be given real responsibility – whether it's commanding a platoon of 30 soldiers on operations or organizing an adventurous training expedition in Arizona.

Officer Cadets spend 44 weeks at the Royal Military Academy Sandhurst being taught all aspects of soldiering as well as transferable leadership, management and communication skills, in a high-pressure environment. After graduating from Sandhurst, they join their chosen Regiment or Corps for further specialist training, before taking command of around 30 soldiers.

Officer Cadets are paid a starting salary of £25,220 while at Sandhurst and this rises to £30,314 on completion of training. Officers can then expect to reach the rank of Captain in 3 years which sees pay increase to £38,847 with annual rises to follow. They also benefit from free health and dental care, subsidised accommodation and food, and a competitive pension.

The Army is one of the largest, most respected graduate employers and offers unrivalled training and development. As well as offering excitement and adventure, the Army supports its officers with continuous professional learning opportunities to further boost their CVs. The Army is looking for people with leadership potential, a strong sense of moral direction and the resourcefulness to succeed.

Those graduates attracted to the idea of becoming an Army officer in their spare time, should consider joining the Army Reserve. The experience gained will be invaluable and they'll get paid for the time spent training – with a bonus payment for completing a certain amount of training days each year.

GRADUATE VACANCIES IN 2015
ENGINEERING
IT
LAW
LOGISTICS

NUMBER OF VACANCIES
650 graduate jobs

LOCATIONS OF VACANCIES

Vacancies also available in Europe and elsewhere in the world.

STARTING SALARY FOR 2015
£25,220

UNIVERSITY VISITS IN 2014-15
ABERDEEN, ASTON, BATH, BELFAST, BIRMINGHAM, BRISTOL, BRUNEL, CAMBRIDGE, CARDIFF, CITY, DUNDEE, DURHAM, EAST ANGLIA, EDINBURGH, EXETER, GLASGOW, IMPERIAL COLLEGE LONDON, KING'S COLLEGE LONDON, LEEDS, LIVERPOOL, LONDON SCHOOL OF ECONOMICS, LOUGHBOROUGH, MANCHESTER, NEWCASTLE, OXFORD, OXFORD BROOKES, QUEEN MARY LONDON, READING, ROYAL HOLLOWAY LONDON, SCHOOL OF AFRICAN STUDIES, SOUTHAMPTON, ST ANDREWS, STRATHCLYDE, SWANSEA, UNIVERSITY COLLEGE LONDON
Please check with your university careers service for full details of local events.

MINIMUM ENTRY REQUIREMENTS
240 UCAS points

APPLICATION DEADLINE
Year-round recruitment

FURTHER INFORMATION
www.Top100GraduateEmployers.com
Register now for the latest news, events information and graduate recruitment details for Britain's leading employers.

A REAL CHALLENGE ISN'T LEADING A MARKETING PRESENTATION, IT'S LEADING THE 30 SOLDIERS UNDER YOUR COMMAND. IT'S LIFTING SPIRITS WHEN HEADS ARE DOWN. IT'S GETTING THEM TO PULL TOGETHER BY KNOWING HOW FAR YOU CAN PUSH THEM. IT'S FOLLOWING YOUR TRAINING SO THAT YOU CAN LEAD BY EXAMPLE.

IT'S BEING AN ARMY OFFICER.

Search armyjobs

ARMY
BE THE BEST

ARUP

An independent firm offering a broad range of professional services, Arup believes that by bringing great people together, there are infinite possibilities. With experts in design, engineering, planning, business consultancy, project management and much more, Arup people work together to shape a better world.

Arup has offices in more than 30 countries across the world, making international team-working part of everyday life and bringing together professionals from diverse disciplines and with complementary skills on a uniquely global scale.

The firm is owned in trust for Arup's employees and this independence translates through the thoughts and actions of its people. Commitment to sustainability is paramount and Arup strives not only to embrace this in projects, but also to embed it into everyday thinking and working.

Graduate opportunities span a wide range of disciplines and offer exceptional experience for individuals who are ambitious, friendly and approach work with fresh eyes and enthusiasm. Arup's diversity helps to foster the creativity that is its hallmark; and the support and freedom for innovation that is encouraged has made Arup the driving force behind some of the most iconic and sustainable designs in the world.

Arup offers competitive benefits and continuous professional development built around employees and their ambitions. Graduates can undertake a professional training programme, accredited by leading organisations such as the Institution of Civil Engineers and the Association for Project Management. As a firm, Arup seeks exceptional people with innovative ideas and curious minds who want to make a real difference to the environment; passion, drive and creativity are a must.

GRADUATE VACANCIES IN 2015

ACCOUNTANCY
CONSULTING
ENGINEERING
FINANCE

NUMBER OF VACANCIES
200+ graduate jobs

LOCATIONS OF VACANCIES

Vacancies also available in Europe, Asia, the USA and elsewhere in the world.

STARTING SALARY FOR 2015
£21,500-£26,500
Plus, up to a £4,000 welcome bonus, and a bi-annual profit share scheme.

UNIVERSITY VISITS IN 2014-15
ABERDEEN, ASTON, BATH, BELFAST, BIRMINGHAM, BRISTOL, CAMBRIDGE, CARDIFF, DURHAM, EXETER, GLASGOW, HERIOT-WATT, IMPERIAL COLLEGE LONDON, LEEDS, LIVERPOOL, LOUGHBOROUGH, MANCHESTER, NEWCASTLE, NOTTINGHAM, OXFORD, SHEFFIELD, SOUTHAMPTON, STRATHCLYDE, SWANSEA, UNIVERSITY COLLEGE LONDON, WARWICK, YORK
Please check with your university careers service for full details of local events.

MINIMUM ENTRY REQUIREMENTS
2.1 Degree
Relevant degree required for some roles.

APPLICATION DEADLINE
Varies by function

FURTHER INFORMATION
www.Top100GraduateEmployers.com
Register now for the latest news, events information and graduate recruitment details for Britain's leading employers.

Infinite possibilities.

At Arup our people are always on the lookout for new and innovative ways to transform the world's infrastructure and built environment. We help to turn the challenges and obstacles of the past into the achievements of the future. We approach our work with fresh eyes and enthusiasm – working to take our industry in exciting directions. This philosophy has helped us design and deliver groundbreaking and iconic work across the world. Involving everyone from design teams and engineers, through consultants, project managers and a myriad of other professions and disciplines.

Early exposure and responsibility is a given. Work life balance is a reality, not an aspiration. And we share our success with everyone – we deliver results collaboratively and we all benefit from those results. It's about making the impossible happen, making a real difference to the world around us. It's about infinite possibilities.

Explore an opportunity where the possibilities are endless...
www.arup.com/ukmeagrads

ARUP
We shape a better world

We are committed to equal opportunities.

ASDA

Like a bolt from the green

Asda is a £multi-billion business with over 170,000 colleagues working in 578 stores and 26 depots. Part of Walmart, the world's largest retailer, it is a major graduate employer in the UK, offering four fast-track programmes, a direct entry route and a huge range of opportunities and benefits.

The four fast-track programmes are: Retail, Trading, Logistics and Rotational. All of them offer an amazing opportunity to make rapid progress through the Asda business, gaining in-depth knowledge, specialist expertise and leadership experience along the way.

Retail graduates can realistically expect to be running their own £1million-a-week Asda stores within three years. For Trading graduates, the goal is Buying Manager within four years, by which time they'll be responsible for £multimillion budgets and negotiating with some of the biggest global brands. While Logistics graduates could well be taking the ideas they've implemented at Asda, across to Walmart and rolling them out across the world.

The Rotational Programme, meanwhile, offers an accelerated route into senior business management via placements in a number of different head office functions. Graduates taking the direct entry route will also join one of these head office functions, which include marketing, property, finance, IT, legal, HR and e-commerce.

Asda has a proven record of developing future business leaders, achieved through a culture where every day is seen as a development opportunity and where every individual counts. Given the rapid progression on offer, not to mention the incredibly fast pace of retail itself, Asda look for graduates who can think on their feet, have a confident and pro-active approach, stay calm under pressure and will hit the ground running every time.

GRADUATE VACANCIES IN 2015
GENERAL MANAGEMENT
LOGISTICS
PURCHASING
RETAILING

NUMBER OF VACANCIES
20-30 graduate jobs

LOCATIONS OF VACANCIES

STARTING SALARY FOR 2015
£24,500

UNIVERSITY VISITS IN 2014-15
BIRMINGHAM, DURHAM, KING'S COLLEGE LONDON, LEEDS, MANCHESTER, NOTTINGHAM, SHEFFIELD, SOUTHAMPTON, YORK
Please check with your university careers service for full details of local events.

MINIMUM ENTRY REQUIREMENTS
Please see website for full details.

APPLICATION DEADLINE
Please see website for full details.

FURTHER INFORMATION
www.Top100GraduateEmployers.com
Register now for the latest news, events information and graduate recruitment details for Britain's leading employers.

TELL US WHERE YOU WANT TO BE

Two-Year Fast-track Graduate Programmes

It may strike you as a bolt from the green, but how would you like to become a future leader in a global organisation? That's what's on offer here. Our graduate programmes provide two years of rising responsibility, increasing challenges and endless opportunities. All so that by the end of it, you'll know exactly where you want to go next.

For a career that will continually take you places, visit **ASDA.jobs/graduates**

It's all on offer

GRADUATE VACANCIES IN 2015

CONSULTING

ENGINEERING

GENERAL MANAGEMENT

IT

PROPERTY

NUMBER OF VACANCIES
300 graduate jobs

LOCATIONS OF VACANCIES

Atkins is one of the world's leading design, engineering and project management consultancies, but prefers to carry on quietly doing brilliant things, letting their achievements speak for themselves. They are involved in some of the world's most technically challenging and time critical projects.

Their work covers a range of sectors including nuclear, oil & gas, power, highways, rail, defence, aerospace, information communications, water, environment, management consultants and design & engineering.

Choosing to start a career with Atkins is more than just selecting where to work. It's about investing in the future and working with other bright minds to produce some truly inspirational projects.

Atkins look for talented engineering graduates from civil, structural, mechanical, electrical, chemical, aerospace and aeronautical, systems and communications as well as buildings, IT, physics, geography and maths to name a few.

Atkins is looking for 300 bright and ambitious graduates to join their award winning Graduate Development Programme. Applicants will be passionate about addressing challenges with creative thinking, and be able to demonstrate flexibility, resilience and drive. Atkins offers an environment in which engineers, planners, architects and a myriad of related professionals flourish. Graduates on the scheme will have access to extensive opportunities across a range of geographical locations, functional disciplines and business areas.

Atkins also offers a range of undergraduate opportunities too. Year-long placements and summer internships to help explore career ideas and focus on future plans, so undergraduates can spend some time with Atkins and get valuable experience and ideas.

Join Atkins to shape the world of tomorrow.

STARTING SALARY FOR 2015
£23,000-£30,000
Plus a settling-in payment and qualification bonus of £5,000.

UNIVERSITY VISITS IN 2014-15
ABERDEEN, BATH, BIRMINGHAM, BRISTOL, CAMBRIDGE, CARDIFF, DURHAM, HERIOT-WATT, IMPERIAL COLLEGE LONDON, LEEDS, LIVERPOOL, LOUGHBOROUGH, MANCHESTER, NEWCASTLE, NOTTINGHAM TRENT, OXFORD, SHEFFIELD, SOUTHAMPTON, STRATHCLYDE, SURREY, UNIVERSITY COLLEGE LONDON, TRINITY COLLEGE DUBLIN, WARWICK
Please check with your university careers service for full details of local events.

MINIMUM ENTRY REQUIREMENTS
2.1 Degree

APPLICATION DEADLINE
Year-round recruitment
Early application advised.

FURTHER INFORMATION
www.Top100GraduateEmployers.com
Register now for the latest news, events information and graduate recruitment details for Britain's leading employers.

This is our story

Quietly doing brilliant things

ΛTKINS

"I wanted to work on some of the most prestigious engineering projects around, across a number of different industries."

Matthew

Graduate and undergraduate opportunities

£competitive pay | Opportunities across the UK

There's more to Atkins than meets the eye. We're the UK's largest engineering consultancy and the biggest multi-disciplinary consultancy in Europe. We're also the seventh largest design firm in the world with a c.£1.4 billion turnover and a global team of around 17,000 brilliant people.

Join us as a graduate or on a placement and you'll broaden your skills and help us to achieve great things, as we take on some of the most exciting engineering challenges of our time.

Amazing projects. Unique challenges. Competitive pay. Your story starts here. Discover more about our opportunities across the UK at

www.atkinsglobal.com /careers/graduates

Plan Design Enable

BAKER & M^cKENZIE

Go –places–

Baker & McKenzie prides itself on being the global law firm that offers a personal and professional approach to its graduates and clients alike. It's this approach that ensures the firm is ideally placed to offer graduates the best possible start to their legal career.

The firm currently operates in over 70 locations across 47 countries and has a presence in all of the world's leading financial centres. The London office, which has been established for over 50 years, is the largest. From here over 400 legal professionals serve a wide and varied network of clients, both in the UK and across the globe.

The global nature of the firm means it offers a great deal of variety to its graduates. It works hard to combine its local legal expertise with the wider experience of its international offices, providing clients with a consistent service and legal professionals the opportunity to interact with colleagues from across the world.

In terms of its client base, Baker & McKenzie works principally with multinational corporations and large financial institutions. Its international scope and client list means the firm is well equipped to act on cross-border transactions and disputes. Baker & McKenzie in London provides the practices that you would expect from one of the world's leading law firms, and is the recognised market leader in many of these.

The firm thrives on new talent. With this in mind, it's not surprising that it makes a significant investment in its graduates and has created an environment where trainees can reach their full potential. Those who enjoy intellectual challenge, are problem solvers and team players with a personable approach will feel at home at this friendly and supportive firm.

GRADUATE VACANCIES IN 2015

LAW

NUMBER OF VACANCIES
30 graduate jobs
For training contracts starting in 2017.

LOCATIONS OF VACANCIES

STARTING SALARY FOR 2015
£39,500
Plus a £3,000 joining bonus.

UNIVERSITY VISITS IN 2014-15
BELFAST, BIRMINGHAM, BRISTOL, CAMBRIDGE, DURHAM, EDINBURGH, EXETER, KING'S COLLEGE LONDON, LEEDS, LEICESTER, LONDON SCHOOL OF ECONOMICS, MANCHESTER, NOTTINGHAM, OXFORD, SOUTHAMPTON, UNIVERSITY COLLEGE LONDON, WARWICK, YORK
Please check with your university careers service for full details of local events.

MINIMUM ENTRY REQUIREMENTS
2.1 Degree

APPLICATION DEADLINE
Varies by function

FURTHER INFORMATION
www.Top100GraduateEmployers.com
Register now for the latest news, events information and graduate recruitment details for Britain's leading employers.

GRADUATE VACANCIES IN 2015
FINANCE
INVESTMENT BANKING
IT

NUMBER OF VACANCIES
200 graduate jobs

LOCATIONS OF VACANCIES

Vacancies also available in Europe.

STARTING SALARY FOR 2015
£Competitive

UNIVERSITY VISITS IN 2014-15
BRISTOL, CAMBRIDGE, CITY, DURHAM, EDINBURGH, IMPERIAL COLLEGE LONDON, KING'S COLLEGE LONDON, LONDON SCHOOL OF ECONOMICS, LOUGHBOROUGH, MANCHESTER, NOTTINGHAM, OXFORD, ST ANDREWS, TRINITY COLLEGE DUBLIN, UNIVERSITY COLLEGE DUBLIN, UNIVERSITY COLLEGE LONDON, WARWICK, YORK
Please check with your university careers service for full details of local events.

MINIMUM ENTRY REQUIREMENTS
2.1 Degree
Relevant degree required for some roles.

APPLICATION DEADLINE
See website for full details.

FURTHER INFORMATION
www.Top100GraduateEmployers.com
Register now for the latest news, events information and graduate recruitment details for Britain's leading employers.

Bank of America is one of the world's leading financial institutions, serving individual consumers, small- and middle-market businesses, large corporations and governments with a full range of financial and risk management products and services. Bank of America Merrill Lynch is the marketing name for the global banking and markets businesses.

The company has had a presence in EMEA since 1922. With offices in 23 countries on three continents, it offers an integrated and comprehensive set of products and services across Global Corporate and Investment Banking, Global Markets and Consumer Card, serving the needs of individual, corporate, institutional and government clients, combining the best of local knowledge and global expertise. Developing solutions for social and environmental challenges is at the core of Bank of America Merrill Lynch's responsibility platform. In more than 90 countries around the world, the company partners with employees, clients and stakeholders to help make financial lives better.

Full-time and internship programmes are available in the following areas: Compliance, Corporate Audit, Global Corporate and Investment Banking, Global Loan Products, Global Markets, Global Transaction Services, Quantitative Management, Research, Risk and Technology – where graduates will gain a breadth of knowledge and experience and be well-positioned for great career opportunities.

By joining Bank of America Merrill Lynch, graduates will receive the highest level of training and mentoring support. Furthermore, the company's commitment to improving the quality of life within the local community and taking care of the environment means that successful applicants will have the opportunity to get involved in a variety of volunteering initiatives.

Where your potential becomes greatness.

At Bank of America Merrill Lynch, we'll match your drive and ambition to where you can make a real impact.

As one of the world's largest financial institutions, our global connections allow you to create a career on your own terms.

We're currently running a range of schemes, including insight programmes, analyst programmes, associate programmes, internships and placements. Discover your potential.

Real Connections. Global Reach.

Get started. Apply today at:
baml.com/campusEMEA

www.barclays.com/joinus

twitter.com/barclaysgrads 🐦 facebook.com/barclaysgraduates f
youtube.com/barclaysgrads ▶ linkedin.com/company/barclays-bank/careers in

It all starts today.

GRADUATE VACANCIES IN 2015

ACCOUNTANCY
FINANCE
GENERAL MANAGEMENT
HUMAN RESOURCES
INVESTMENT BANKING
IT
MARKETING

NUMBER OF VACANCIES
200+ graduate jobs

LOCATIONS OF VACANCIES

Vacancies also available in Europe, Asia, the USA and elsewhere in the world.

STARTING SALARY FOR 2015
£Competitive

UNIVERSITY VISITS IN 2014-15
BATH, BIRMINGHAM, BRISTOL,
CAMBRIDGE, DURHAM, EDINBURGH,
EXETER, GLASGOW, IMPERIAL COLLEGE
LONDON, KING'S COLLEGE LONDON,
LEEDS, LEICESTER, LONDON SCHOOL
OF ECONOMICS, LOUGHBOROUGH,
MANCHESTER, NOTTINGHAM, OXFORD,
READING, SOUTHAMPTON, ST ANDREWS,
STRATHCLYDE, UNIVERSITY COLLEGE
LONDON, WARWICK
*Please check with your university careers
service for full details of local events.*

APPLICATION DEADLINE
Varies by function

FURTHER INFORMATION
www.Top100GraduateEmployers.com
*Register now for the latest news, events
information and graduate recruitment
details for Britain's leading employers.*

Barclays is a bank with strong values and a clear purpose: helping people achieve their ambitions – in the right way. That starts with its graduates, from day one. Right across Barclays, graduates are playing a part in realising the vision of the firm and in so doing, driving their own careers too.

Those joining can expect immediate responsibility, whichever area they join. Their development will focus on building their individual strengths, learning through challenging work and rewarding roles, supported by training and professional education. They will also be encouraged to explore innovative thinking to inspire progress.

Every background and every degree discipline is welcome: Barclays offers a remarkable breadth of career opportunities for students, undergraduates, graduates and postgraduates. As well as a strong academic record and a commercial outlook, new graduates coming into Barclays need to be ready to express their ideas, effect change, learn quickly and make an impact.

As an organisation, Barclays has a long tradition of innovation that remains at the heart of the business to this day. Already a major international financial services provider, with approximately 140,000 people working in more than 50 countries, Barclays is reshaping and rebalancing its business to build on its strengths. There are now four core businesses: Personal and Corporate Banking, the Investment Bank, Barclaycard and Africa. It is a strong foundation from which to grow. Graduates will find opportunities across each of these businesses, as well as in the vital business functions such as Technology, Risk, Operations and Compliance.

Barclays' ambition is clear – to become both the instinctive partner of choice for all its stakeholders, and the best place for graduates to start their careers.

Go a long way,
the right way.

Graduate and internship opportunities

As we set out to shape the future of Barclays, we are looking to our
graduates and interns to play their part. Whichever part of the business
you join, your innovation, drive and inspiration will take us forward.
You'll get every opportunity to make a positive impact, and our full
support when you do. And it all starts today.

barclays.com/joinus

BBC

GRADUATE VACANCIES IN 2015

ENGINEERING
IT
MEDIA
RESEARCH & DEVELOPMENT

NUMBER OF VACANCIES
50+ graduate jobs

LOCATIONS OF VACANCIES

The BBC is one of the world's best-known broadcasting brands. Roughly 96% of UK adults use its services each week – not to mention millions more around the globe. The corporation wants to offer these people a future that is truly interactive, on-demand and online, and so needs the best graduates to help make it happen.

There are trainee opportunities in everything from journalism and production to industry-leading technology. Production or Journalism trainees at the BBC are the foundation of the corporation's quality broadcasting and might help shape the future of news programming or maybe create the next Doctor Who or Top Gear. Whereas, Technology or Research & Development trainees have the unique chance to be part of some of the nation's most innovative and popular digital products. Think the BBC News, Weather and Sport apps, iPlayer, or the new BBC Playlister.

Graduates that join the BBC on the Production, Journalism, Technology or Research & Development schemes will spend one to two years receiving some of the best training in the industry, learning, growing and breaking new ground. Digital Media Graduates, for example, are supported from aspiring developer to industry expert, and BBC Technology Trainees earn a Masters in Digital Broadcast Technology.

Production and Journalism trainees work in our UK newsrooms and production teams, adding new and exciting ideas for broadcast. And that's just a taste of the numerous career paths a trainee can forge as a graduate at the BBC.

No matter which scheme is chosen, BBC trainees are in a position to make a real mark on the nation's culture and their career prospects.

STARTING SALARY FOR 2015
£22,000-£25,000

UNIVERSITY VISITS IN 2014-15
Please check with your university careers service for full details of local events.

MINIMUM ENTRY REQUIREMENTS
Relevant degree required for some roles.

APPLICATION DEADLINE
Varies by function

FURTHER INFORMATION
www.Top100GraduateEmployers.com
Register now for the latest news, events information and graduate recruitment details for Britain's leading employers.

Help create the future of the BBC
Graduate Opportunities | UK Wide | £20,000 – £25,000 pa

The BBC is one of the world's best-known broadcasting brands. 96% of UK adults use our services each week – not to mention millions more around the globe. We want to offer them a future that is interactive, on-demand and online, and we need the best graduates to help make it happen – from journalism to production to our industry-leading technology teams.

As a Production or Journalism Trainee, you can shape the future of the BBC's news programming or maybe help to create the next Doctor Who or Top Gear.

As a Technology or Research & Development Trainee, you'll have the unique chance to be a part of some of the nation's most innovative and popular products, such as our News, Weather and Sport apps, iPlayer and the new BBC Playlister.

No matter which of our schemes you'll join, you'll receive excellent training and development and in turn help us transform the way media is consumed by creating ground-breaking broadcasting experiences.

To find out more visit **www.bbc.co.uk/careers/trainee-schemes**

The world's watching

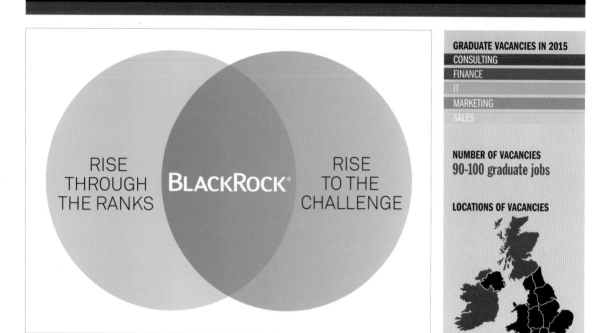

BLACKROCK®

GRADUATE VACANCIES IN 2015

CONSULTING
FINANCE
IT
MARKETING
SALES

NUMBER OF VACANCIES
90-100 graduate jobs

LOCATIONS OF VACANCIES

Vacancies also available in Europe, Asia and the USA.

STARTING SALARY FOR 2015
£Competitive

UNIVERSITY VISITS IN 2014-15
BATH, BRISTOL, CAMBRIDGE, DURHAM, EDINBURGH, GLASGOW, IMPERIAL COLLEGE LONDON, KING'S COLLEGE LONDON, LEEDS, LONDON SCHOOL OF ECONOMICS, MANCHESTER, NOTTINGHAM, OXFORD, ST ANDREWS, TRINITY COLLEGE DUBLIN, UNIVERSITY COLLEGE DUBLIN, UNIVERSITY COLLEGE LONDON, WARWICK
Please check with your university careers service for full details of local events.

MINIMUM ENTRY REQUIREMENTS
2.1 Degree

APPLICATION DEADLINE
16th November 2014

FURTHER INFORMATION
www.Top100GraduateEmployers.com
Register now for the latest news, events information and graduate recruitment details for Britain's leading employers.

As the world's largest asset manager, BlackRock brings together financial leadership, worldwide reach and state-of-the-art technology to provide answers to the millions of investors from across the globe who entrust their financial futures to the company.

At BlackRock a collaborative culture unites all the business groups – as does a common focus on helping the firm's clients and the communities in which BlackRock employees work and live. BlackRock seeks the best and brightest talent to join a dynamic and diverse environment that inspires high performance.

The Graduate Programme at BlackRock is an ideal opportunity for natural-born problem solvers, innovators and future leaders to work for a firm that has been called in by some of the world's largest companies and governments to find solutions for their most pressing financial challenges.

BlackRock is committed to harnessing every graduate's potential, developing their expertise and advancing their career. All members of the Graduate Programme begin their BlackRock career with a two-week orientation in New York. Following this, graduates benefit from a structured curriculum of ongoing training throughout the first year and beyond, all designed to maximise their business knowledge and individual effectiveness.

Over the last 26 years BlackRock has built up a network of more than 60 offices worldwide, including London, Edinburgh, Paris, Frankfurt, Zurich, Milan, New York, San Francisco and Hong Kong, which gives graduates ample room to move across businesses and boarders. As a global firm, the work is diverse and the opportunities are limitless, with positions in Advisory, Analytics & Risk, Client Businesses, Corporate Operations, Investment and Technology.

MAKE A
LIVING

BLACKROCK®

MAKE A
DIFFERENCE

The world is more complex than ever before. And with the financial futures of millions in our hands, we're looking for the best and brightest talent – the future leaders that will help make a difference for our clients and the larger world around us. From Advisory and Client Support to Investment Management and Technology – no matter what you're looking to do, there are many exciting challenges waiting for you at BlackRock.

Meet our people and find out how you can make a difference at BlackRock at **blackrockoncampus.com**

BLACKROCK®

INVESTING FOR A NEW WORLD™

jobs.bloomberg.com
facebook.com/BloombergCareers
linkedin.com/company/2494 twitter.com/bloombergcareer

Bloomberg

Bloomberg delivers critical information, in a world where information matters. Bloomberg gives influential decision-makers in business, finance and government a competitive edge by connecting them to a dynamic network of news, people and ideas.

In a world where fast, accurate, trusted information is crucial, Bloomberg gives decision makers in business, finance and government a competitive edge by connecting them to a dynamic network of news, people and ideas. Bloomberg delivers data, facts and analytics through constantly evolving technology – quickly and accurately – so Bloomberg clients can move first. From stocks, bonds and currencies to companies, industries and economies, Bloomberg is at the centre of the action.

The Bloomberg Professional® service sits at the core of its network. With more than 315,000 active subscribers, Bloomberg provide unmatched visibility into global and local financial markets and the world of business, with a mission to always be first.

Bloomberg's media services – television, print, radio and online – support and enhance its core offerings, with more than 2,400 news and multimedia professionals at 146 bureaus in 72 countries.

What does it mean to work at Bloomberg? It's about becoming part of something as big as set ambitions. This is an energetic place to begin a career – or to propel it forward.

Being a crucial part of important decisions across an entire planet means Bloomberg is growing: entering new markets, launching new ventures, pushing boundaries. This is an exciting moment for Bloomberg, with major, worldwide opportunities to be seized.

GRADUATE VACANCIES IN 2015
FINANCE
IT
SALES

NUMBER OF VACANCIES
300+ graduate jobs

LOCATIONS OF VACANCIES

STARTING SALARY FOR 2015
£Competitive
Plus benefits.

UNIVERSITY VISITS IN 2014-15
ASTON, BATH, BIRMINGHAM, BRISTOL, CAMBRIDGE, CARDIFF, CITY, DURHAM, EDINBURGH, GLASGOW, IMPERIAL COLLEGE LONDON, KING'S COLLEGE LONDON, LEEDS, LONDON SCHOOL OF ECONOMICS, MANCHESTER, NOTTINGHAM, OXFORD, QUEEN MARY LONDON, SOUTHAMPTON, TRINITY COLLEGE DUBLIN, UNIVERSITY COLLEGE DUBLIN, UNIVERSITY COLLEGE LONDON, WARWICK, YORK
Please check with your university careers service for full details of local events.

APPLICATION DEADLINE
Year-round recruitment

FURTHER INFORMATION
www.Top100GraduateEmployers.com
Register now for the latest news, events information and graduate recruitment details for Britain's leading employers.

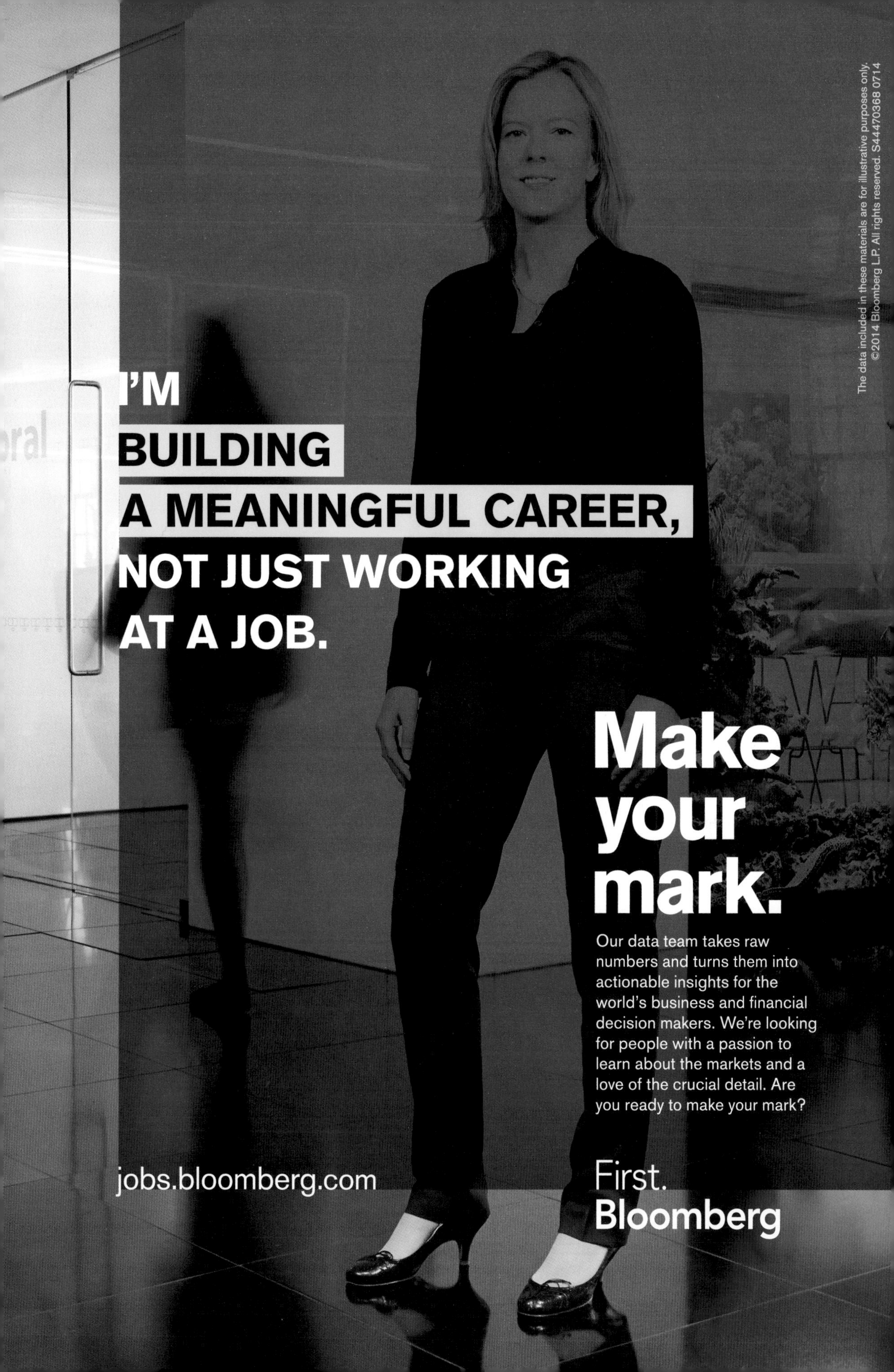
I'M
BUILDING
A MEANINGFUL CAREER,
NOT JUST WORKING
AT A JOB.
Make your mark.
Our data team takes raw numbers and turns them into actionable insights for the world's business and financial decision makers. We're looking for people with a passion to learn about the markets and a love of the crucial detail. Are you ready to make your mark?
jobs.bloomberg.com
First.
Bloomberg
The data included in these materials are for illustrative purposes only.
©2014 Bloomberg L.P. All rights reserved. S444703680714

Boots

SO MANY REASONS WHY BOOTS IS #Good4Grads

As the UK's leading pharmacy-led health and beauty retailer and one of the country's most trusted household names, Boots is evolving in the changing world of retail and our future looks very bright. The company needs to develop future leaders who genuinely love driving business performance by creating "feel good" moments for customers.

On the Boots Graduate Programme there are six exciting, involving and evolving areas of the business to choose from. The Retail Management Programme develops graduates as store leaders capable of offering Boots customers the legendary experience they expect each time they walk into a store. On the Brand, Buying and Marketing Programme, candidates will explore how to develop, source and market Boots' renowned brands, as well as a range of external brands.

The Finance Programme offers graduates more than just experience in financial accounting, management information and business partnering. They'll be part of the department creating the business framework for now and the future. Boots will also fund a relevant qualification and offer the opportunity to work in an international role. On the Technology Leadership Programme, graduates will be driving IT solutions to meet the demands of this fast growing business now and in the future.

This year Boots also have programmes in Supply Chain and Operations. Graduates will see how the business responds to the ever-changing customer needs and drives loyalty & sales to increase market share. It's a big operation and this is a big opportunity.

What's really important for all our programmes is a passion for retail and a desire to drive the business into the future. Develop an amazing career with Boots and realise why the company is #Good4Grads.

GRADUATE VACANCIES IN 2015

ACCOUNTANCY
FINANCE
GENERAL MANAGEMENT
IT
LOGISTICS
MARKETING
PURCHASING
RETAILING

NUMBER OF VACANCIES
60 graduate jobs

LOCATIONS OF VACANCIES

STARTING SALARY FOR 2015
£25,000
Plus a £1,000 welcome payment.

UNIVERSITY VISITS IN 2014-15
Please check with your university careers service for full details of local events.

MINIMUM ENTRY REQUIREMENTS
2.2 Degree
280 UCAS points

APPLICATION DEADLINE
Year-round recruitment

FURTHER INFORMATION
www.Top100GraduateEmployers.com
Register now for the latest news, events information and graduate recruitment details for Britain's leading employers.

www.bcglondon.com

facebook.com/BCGinLondon **f**   lonrecruiting@bcg.com ✉

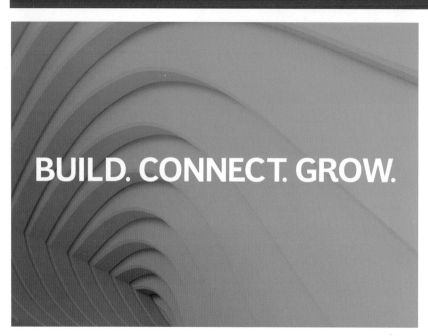

BUILD. CONNECT. GROW.

GRADUATE VACANCIES IN 2015

CONSULTING

NUMBER OF VACANCIES
No fixed quota

LOCATIONS OF VACANCIES

STARTING SALARY FOR 2015
£Competitive

UNIVERSITY VISITS IN 2014-15
CAMBRIDGE, IMPERIAL COLLEGE LONDON,
LONDON SCHOOL OF ECONOMICS,
OXFORD, TRINITY COLLEGE DUBLIN,
UNIVERSITY COLLEGE DUBLIN,
UNIVERSITY COLLEGE LONDON
*Please check with your university careers
service for full details of local events.*

MINIMUM ENTRY REQUIREMENTS
2.1 Degree

APPLICATION DEADLINE
1st November 2014

FURTHER INFORMATION
www.Top100GraduateEmployers.com
*Register now for the latest news, events
information and graduate recruitment
details for Britain's leading employers.*

The Boston Consulting Group (BCG) is a global management consulting firm with more than 80 offices in 45 countries. BCG pioneers ideas that drive sustained competitive advantage across all sectors and regions, and transform clients, industries, and society.

BCG is a diverse place: there are many reasons to join this company, but ultimately, it's about three elements:

Building impact: In an increasingly complex world, BCG goes deep to unlock insight and have the courage to act. BCG is partner and trusted advisor to the world's most influential businesses, governments, and non-profits. The company helps them respond to today's incredible pace of change to stay competitive and add value to society. With BCG, graduates will learn how to navigate complexity, draw unique insights, facilitate change and become a leader responsible for real and lasting impact.

Connecting aspirations: It's pretty simple – BCGers genuinely want to help their clients and each other succeed. Challenged by mentors and supported by teams, graduates will join a diverse group of highly driven, exceptional individuals who respect and trust each other. In a culture where ideas are heard regardless of tenure, the deep relationships they develop with clients and colleagues will become a foundation for their future endeavours.

Growing leaders: for graduates to truly develop themselves, they have to challenge established thinking. They have to seek a better way. Supported by the global team of BCG experts across a breadth of topics, their careers will dramatically accelerate through faster learning and rapid advancement. What graduates experience will help them find deep personal meaning as they develop a platform for future success.

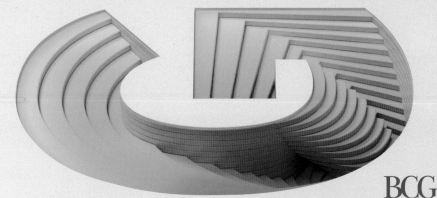

BCG
THE BOSTON CONSULTING GROUP

BUILDING IMPACT.
CONNECTING ASPIRATIONS.
GROWING LEADERS.

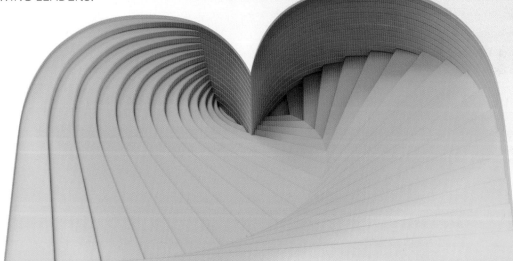

BUILD. CONNECT. GROW. BCG.COM/CAREERS

bp

I FOUND A NEW WAY TO GET INTO POLE POSITION

OLIVER TAYLOR, ENGINEERING, PANGBOURNE, UK

Heat. Light. Power. Mobility. Materials for the products that define modern life. All are made possible by oil and gas. Delivering them safely, sustainably and cost effectively is what BP's business is all about. And remains one of the biggest challenges in the world today.

BP offers graduate opportunities in engineering, science, business and trading. Successful applicants will find out what it takes to deliver energy safely to the world and discover how BP and its people find, develop and produce essential sources of energy and how that energy is turned into products everyone on the planet depends on every day.

Graduates who join BP will find out how BP's people make some truly amazing discoveries to meet that challenge. Both in terms of scientific and engineering breakthroughs and what BP as a team are capable of.

BP recruits ambitious graduates at every stage of the energy life cycle – from geoscientists sending shock waves through the earth to find new oil and gas reserves and engineers building platforms in the ocean to extract them, to traders anticipating and reacting to changes in the markets around them.

Designed for future business leaders, world-class scientists or ground-breaking engineers, BP's graduate programmes are designed to help students develop the skills and experience they need. And at the same time, they get a unique insight into BP's work and discover how incredible an organisation it is to be part of.

Because BP offers such a breadth of opportunity in engineering, science, business and trading, students could come to BP with a good degree in practically any discipline. Every bit as important will be the individual attributes and personal qualities students bring.

GRADUATE VACANCIES IN 2015
ACCOUNTANCY
ENGINEERING
FINANCE
GENERAL MANAGEMENT
HUMAN RESOURCES
INVESTMENT BANKING
IT
LOGISTICS
PURCHASING
RESEARCH & DEVELOPMENT
RETAILING
SALES

NUMBER OF VACANCIES
150 graduate jobs

LOCATIONS OF VACANCIES

STARTING SALARY FOR 2015
£33,000+
Plus a £3,000 settling-in allowance.

UNIVERSITY VISITS IN 2014-15
BATH, BIRMINGHAM, CAMBRIDGE, DURHAM, IMPERIAL COLLEGE LONDON, MANCHESTER, NOTTINGHAM, OXFORD, STRATHCLYDE
Please check with your university careers service for full details of local events.

MINIMUM ENTRY REQUIREMENTS
2.1 Degree

APPLICATION DEADLINE
Varies by function

FURTHER INFORMATION
www.Top100GraduateEmployers.com
Register now for the latest news, events information and graduate recruitment details for Britain's leading employers.

I DISCOVERED TO BE AN EXPERT

MEANS ALWAYS BEING A STUDENT

It's amazing how much I've learned working with BP. The sites I've visited, people I've met and projects I've worked on have helped prepare me for my current role – and inspired me to carry on growing.

UNI HONG, BUSINESS AND TRADING, SINGAPORE

What will you discover?

t BP, we offer the most exciting and challenging global opportunities for high erforming graduates in engineering, science, business and trading.

earch for BP Careers

bp

GRADUATE VACANCIES IN 2015

CONSULTING
ENGINEERING
GENERAL MANAGEMENT
HUMAN RESOURCES
IT
LOGISTICS
PURCHASING
RESEARCH & DEVELOPMENT

NUMBER OF VACANCIES
75+ graduate jobs

LOCATIONS OF VACANCIES

STARTING SALARY FOR 2015
£27,000-£31,250

UNIVERSITY VISITS IN 2014-15
CAMBRIDGE, DURHAM, IMPERIAL COLLEGE
LONDON, LEEDS, LONDON SCHOOL
OF ECONOMICS, LOUGHBOROUGH,
MANCHESTER, OXFORD, SHEFFIELD,
SOUTHAMPTON, UNIVERSITY COLLEGE
LONDON, WARWICK
*Please check with your university careers
service for full details of local events.*

MINIMUM ENTRY REQUIREMENTS
2.1 Degree

APPLICATION DEADLINE
Please see website for full details.

FURTHER INFORMATION
www.Top100GraduateEmployers.com
*Register now for the latest news, events
information and graduate recruitment
details for Britain's leading employers.*

BA, part of International Airlines Group, is one of the world's leading global premium airlines and the largest international carrier in the UK. The carrier has its home base at London Heathrow, the world's busiest international airport, and flies to more than 70 different countries.

BA carries almost 40 million customers a year and has a fleet of more than 280 aircraft. If the past decade has brought both challenge and opportunity, it's the future which genuinely excites. BA is on a journey, a journey its people live, feel and shape each day. And the journey they're on is to be experienced – because few organisations inspire such belonging, purpose and genuine belief.

BA is a business with breadth and complexity and at its heart are its people. Graduates joining BA will be a key part of this journey that's about a greater purpose; the promise BA makes to each of its customers every day: To Fly. To Serve.

Graduates who join BA work on real jobs with real responsibilities. This takes ambition, resilience, and the drive to go above and beyond. They can expect to work across different business areas, to be involved in key business decisions and have opportunities to travel and to work in different locations. With attractive colleague travel benefits BA's graduates all have the opportunity to see the world and share unique experiences.

There are opportunities to become one of their Analysts or Leaders for Business as well as in IT, HR, Procurement, Operational Research, Engineering and World Cargo. Whichever career path is taken, each will start with a comprehensive induction. Then each programme has its own structured development plan to make sure graduates have all the support and opportunities they need to excel and live the journey.

LIVE THE JOURNEY

We're a unique organisation on a unique journey. With a brand that inspires both affection and recognition the world over, we're building a future based on unrivalled insight, expertise and passion with people who believe so deeply in what they do that they wouldn't dream of being anywhere else. You can join us. Whether you want to work as a graduate in IT, HR, Procurement, Operational Research, Engineering, World Cargo or become one of our Analysts or Leaders for Business, you'll join our journey, as we invest £5bn in making air travel easier, more efficient, more enjoyable, and more sustainable. You'll fuel a fleet that travels the world. Your eagerness, imagination, and relentlessness will shape our future. A future to remind everyone what the British Airways name stands for. **Live the journey.**
www.britishairways.com/careers

BRITISH SUGAR

An **AB Sugar** Company

www.notjustsugar.com

EXCEEDING
YOUR
expectations

British Sugar is the UK's leading supplier of sugar to the UK market, processing the country's entire annual sugar beet crop of 7.5 million tonnes, extracting over 1 million tonnes of sugar and producing an additional 500,000 tonnes of animal feed from sugar beet pulp each year.

Located in East Anglia and the East Midlands, its four state-of-the-art processing plants match anything in the oil, chemical and power industries. Using a highly integrated approach to manufacturing, British Sugar develops and sells a diverse range of sustainable products.

Sugar production remains at the core of its operations, but using a highly integrated approach to manufacturing, British Sugar aims to transform all of its raw materials into sustainable products. Using its Combined Heat & Power plants, the organisation exports enough electricity for 160,000 homes and uses the combustion gases to grow around 140 million tomatoes and invested in the UK's first Bioethanol plant, producing 70 million litres of renewable fuel.

The company regularly recruits graduates for a range of challenging roles within engineering, science, agriculture, finance and business management, based at its processing plants or the Central Office in Peterborough.

British Sugar is part of AB Sugar. The company that has grown into one of the largest sugar producers in the world, employing more than 42,000 people and operating in 10 countries with a production capacity of around 5 million tonnes of sugar each year from both beet and cane.

AB Sugar is wholly owned by international food, ingredients and retail group, Associated British Foods plc, with a portfolio of well-known brands including Allinson, Blue Dragon, Pataks, Primark and Twinings.

GRADUATE VACANCIES
ACCOUNTANCY
ENGINEERING
FINANCE
GENERAL MANAGEMENT
LOGISTICS
PURCHASING
SALES

NUMBER OF VACANCIES
No fixed quota

LOCATIONS OF VACANCIES

STARTING SALARY
£25,000-£30,000
Plus a £1,500 joining bonus.

UNIVERSITY VISITS IN 2014-15
Please check with your university careers service for full details of local events.

MINIMUM ENTRY REQUIREMENTS
2.1 Degree

APPLICATION DEADLINE
Please see website for full details.

FURTHER INFORMATION
www.Top100GraduateEmployers.com
Register now for the latest news, events information and graduate recruitment details for Britain's leading employers.

OPPORTUNITY **ENGINEERING** **AGRICULTURE**

GROWTH **NURTURE** **CHALLENGE**

ENERGY **INNOVATION** **TALENT**

BRITISH SUGAR

GROW WITH US

British Sugar is the UK's leading sugar supplier to food and drink manufacturers in the UK and Europe, and with around 4,000 growers supplying its four factories the business produces over 1 million tonnes of sugar each year. Graduates are at the heart of British Sugars talent pool and stand out for their passion, drive, adaptability, a desire to challenge and a can-do attitude.

Beyond sugar production there is a surprisingly diverse business to be discovered.

British Sugar is part of AB Sugar, which is wholly owned by international food, ingredients and retail group, Associated British Foods plc.

Your future starts here.

For an insight into British Sugar visit:

NOTJUSTSUGAR.COM

Welcome to a world of innovation. BT are one of the world's leading providers of innovative technology and communication services. They're always looking for new ways to help businesses and people across the globe by developing new technologies that make amazing things happen.

But staying ahead in the industry isn't just about technology. It's about people too. People who want to challenge the norm, think of new and better ways to do things and work as part of a team to make them happen. Diversity is at the very heart of the company. In order to provide the very best products and services to their varied customer base they need a diverse workforce to imagine, create and deliver the solutions required both now and into the future. This means creating a working environment that includes and recognises such diversity.

So what makes a successful BT graduate? Leadership potential? Teamworking ability? Creativity? Enthusiasm? Ambition? BT looks for all of these qualities. And more. They look for people who don't wait to be told what to do, and who can't wait to get involved.

BT graduates work on real projects, with real responsibility from the start. Whatever they're involved in – whether it's technology, business management, marketing, sales, or legal – they're encouraged to take the initiative.

It's about taking talent and developing future leaders. Throughout the programme, graduates benefit from ongoing training, both on the job and in the classroom. From talent masterclasses, through to leadership development and commercial awareness, every opportunity is there to be seized. There's huge scope for graduates to shape their own career. To make the most of their leadership potential. And to help BT make more amazing things happen.

GRADUATE VACANCIES IN 2015
CONSULTING
ENGINEERING
GENERAL MANAGEMENT
IT
LAW
MARKETING
RESEARCH & DEVELOPMENT
SALES

NUMBER OF VACANCIES
200 graduate jobs

LOCATIONS OF VACANCIES

STARTING SALARY FOR 2015
£27,500-£31,500

UNIVERSITY VISITS IN 2014-15
ASTON, BATH, BIRMINGHAM, BRISTOL, CAMBRIDGE, DURHAM, EDINBURGH, ESSEX, GLASGOW, IMPERIAL COLLEGE LONDON, KING'S COLLEGE LONDON, LANCASTER, LEEDS, LOUGHBOROUGH, MANCHESTER, NOTTINGHAM, OXFORD, SHEFFIELD, SOUTHAMPTON, STRATHCLYDE, WARWICK, YORK
Please check with your university careers service for full details of local events.

MINIMUM ENTRY REQUIREMENTS
2.1 Degree
280-320 UCAS points

APPLICATION DEADLINE
Varies by function

FURTHER INFORMATION
www.Top100GraduateEmployers.com
Register now for the latest news, events information and graduate recruitment details for Britain's leading employers.

Make amazing things happen.

BT's technology helps make amazing things happen across the globe. But staying ahead in the industry is about more than just technology; it's about people too.

As a BT graduate you'll turn amazing ideas into real life solutions that help people connect, communicate and collaborate better than ever before.

Visit **www.btgraduates.com** to find out more.

CANCER RESEARCH UK

IT'LL TAKE SMART, SHARP MINDED PEOPLE TO HELP US BEAT CANCER SOONER.

PEOPLE LIKE YOU.

GRADUATE VACANCIES IN 2015

FINANCE
GENERAL MANAGEMENT
HUMAN RESOURCES
IT
MARKETING
RESEARCH & DEVELOPMENT

NUMBER OF VACANCIES
8 graduate jobs

LOCATIONS OF VACANCIES

STARTING SALARY FOR 2015
£24,000

UNIVERSITY VISITS IN 2014-15
CAMBRIDGE, EXETER, IMPERIAL COLLEGE LONDON, KING'S COLLEGE LONDON, LEEDS, OXFORD, READING, SOUTHAMPTON, ST ANDREWS, UNIVERSITY COLLEGE LONDON, WARWICK, YORK
Please check with your university careers service for full details of local events.

MINIMUM ENTRY REQUIREMENTS
2.1 Degree

APPLICATION DEADLINE
January 2015

FURTHER INFORMATION
www.Top100GraduateEmployers.com
Register now for the latest news, events information and graduate recruitment details for Britain's leading employers.

Cancer. Be afraid. Cancer Research UK is a world-leading organisation and a prestigious funder of science. Day after day, it works to find new and better ways to prevent, detect and treat cancer. Its vision is to bring forward the day when all cancers are cured.

Every step the charity makes towards beating cancer sooner relies on every person, every team and every effort. Now they are looking for smart, sharp minded individuals to continue to achieve their goals. Its graduates are passionate in their work, relentlessly determined, unafraid to challenge, stand-out communicators and effective relationship-builders. Not to mention, ready and willing to make a real contribution to bring Cancer Research UK closer to its bold ambition.

What does a graduate scheme at an organisation like this offer? All graduates are put through their paces from the very beginning. Whether joining Cancer Research UK's Fundraising and Marketing; Science Strategy and Funding; IT and Digital; Policy Information and Communications or Finance and Corporate streams, they will have the exciting opportunity to rotate across four business areas over the course of the two years.

Graduates receive support and challenge from senior mentors, peers and placement managers along their journey. They also benefit from a combination of on-the-job learning and formal training whilst transitioning between placements. Graduates are expected to gain a permanent job at the end of the scheme, subject to performance and business need.

As well as graduate opportunities, Cancer Research UK offers a vast array of volunteering opportunities including award-winning twelve-week internships.

Join Cancer Research UK and help beat cancer sooner.

AMBITIOUS
SMART FAST-PACED
INSPIRING
DRIVING SHARP
CHANGE
UNITED
PIONEERING
VERSATILE CHALLENGING
LIFE-SAVING PERCEPTIONS

THIS IS HOW IT FEELS HELPING TO BEAT CANCER.
For your chance to experience it, go to cruk.org/graduates

CANCER
RESEARCH
UK

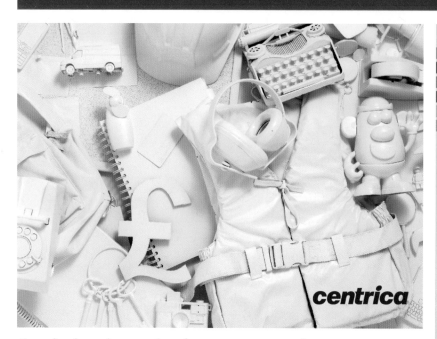

Centrica is an international energy company that sources, generates, processes, stores, trades, supplies, services and helps its customers save energy. Securing energy to power the future is an important priority for Centrica, and the company is making vital investments across the entire energy spectrum.

As a top 30 FTSE 100 company with over 30 million customer accounts, a £26.6 billion turnover and more than 37,000 employees, Centrica is the parent company for a range of global brands. British Gas and Direct Energy supply power and related services in the UK and North America respectively; Direct Energy and Centrica Energy in the UK manage power generation, gas and oil production and trading operations to ensure day-to-day demand is met, and Centrica Storage is the largest gas storage facility in the UK.

Graduates could be getting involved in any area of the energy lifecycle – from exploration and production with Centrica Energy, to front-line customer service management at British Gas – although the exact role will depend on which of the schemes they join. The graduate programme has been designed to offer a broad grounding in the business; those who are ambitious and commercially savvy have an outstanding opportunity to be a future business leader in this diverse organisation.

Developing graduates is important to Centrica; graduate talent boards ensure they have the opportunity to fulfil their potential and are equipped with the right skills and behaviours to help grow the business and implement Centrica's strategy. It all adds up to an award-winning programme that offers graduates who are up for big challenges the opportunity to get involved in a variety of areas – as well as receiving support and reward along the way.

GRADUATE VACANCIES IN 2015

ENGINEERING
FINANCE
GENERAL MANAGEMENT
HUMAN RESOURCES
IT
MARKETING

NUMBER OF VACANCIES
60+ graduate jobs

LOCATIONS OF VACANCIES

STARTING SALARY FOR 2015
£Competitive

UNIVERSITY VISITS IN 2014-15
BIRMINGHAM, BRISTOL, CAMBRIDGE, IMPERIAL COLLEGE LONDON, LONDON SCHOOL OF ECONOMICS, MANCHESTER, OXFORD, SOUTHAMPTON, WARWICK
Please check with your university careers service for full details of local events.

MINIMUM ENTRY REQUIREMENTS
Relevant degree required for some roles.

APPLICATION DEADLINE
Varies by function

FURTHER INFORMATION
www.Top100GraduateEmployers.com
Register now for the latest news, events information and graduate recruitment details for Britain's leading employers.

Be part **of it all.**

  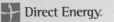

Since Citi opened its first office in New York in 1812, it has answered the needs of economies, businesses and communities in hundreds of cities, in over 160 countries, thriving in the most challenging times over a 200 year history. Citi's global presence isn't just a question of size, it's a way of thinking.

Citi's success is driven by its exceptional people – their passion, dedication and entrepreneurship – and it will be people with these qualities who will shape its future. At Citi, learning doesn't stop at graduation and they provide one of the best learning and development programmes in banking. Whatever the degree there is a chance to excel at Citi and become of part global firm that provides the most forward-thinking financial products and solutions to the most enterprising corporations, institutions, governments and individuals around the world.

Citi offers full-time, placement and internship opportunities across a number of its business areas, including Investment Banking, Corporate Banking, Capital Markets Origination, Markets and Securities Services, Treasury and Trade Solutions (TTS), Investment Research, Private Bank, Risk Management, Human Resources, Operations and Technology.

Citi also offers insight programmes enabling students in their first year (or in their second year of a four year course) to experience first-hand the Citi culture and environment. The most successful candidates on these programmes will also secure an assessment centre for a place on the following years internship.

Graduates interested in this industry with drive, commitment and a passion for learning are encouraged to apply. This is the opportunity to be part of an exciting period in the development of the global financial services industry, working with the brightest minds to drive responsible, positive change within Citi and beyond.

GRADUATE VACANCIES IN 2015
HUMAN RESOURCES
INVESTMENT BANKING
IT

NUMBER OF VACANCIES
180-220 graduate jobs

LOCATIONS OF VACANCIES

Vacancies also available in Europe and elsewhere in the world.

STARTING SALARY FOR 2015
£Competitive

UNIVERSITY VISITS IN 2014-15
BATH, BRISTOL, CAMBRIDGE, CITY, DURHAM, EDINBURGH, EXETER, IMPERIAL COLLEGE LONDON, KING'S COLLEGE LONDON, LEEDS, LONDON SCHOOL OF ECONOMICS, LOUGHBOROUGH, MANCHESTER, NOTTINGHAM, OXFORD, QUEEN MARY LONDON, ST ANDREWS, TRINITY COLLEGE DUBLIN, UNIVERSITY COLLEGE DUBLIN, UNIVERSITY COLLEGE LONDON, WARWICK
Please check with your university careers service for full details of local events.

MINIMUM ENTRY REQUIREMENTS
2.1 Degree
320 UCAS points

APPLICATION DEADLINE
Year-round recruitment
Early application advised.

FURTHER INFORMATION
www.Top100GraduateEmployers.com
Register now for the latest news, events information and graduate recruitment details for Britain's leading employers.

start your career here

Are you bright and ambitious?
Do you relish a challenge?
Do you want to work in a global
company that encourages
innovation and diversity?

Then consider Citi.

Here at Citi we provide one of the best
graduate training programmes in the
industry. So whatever your background,
you can excel with us!

Whether you're a student in your first
or final year, we have a programme for
you. Visit our website to learn how to
start your career at Citi.

your place is here

f 🐦 /citigradsEMEA
oncampus.citi.com

citi®

"I want to have
an impact on people,
not just the bottom line."

Ailsa Harris, Generalist Fast Stream

GRADUATE VACANCIES IN 2015

FINANCE

GENERAL MANAGEMENT

HUMAN RESOURCES

IT

MARKETING

RESEARCH & DEVELOPMENT

NUMBER OF VACANCIES
800+ graduate jobs

LOCATIONS OF VACANCIES

STARTING SALARY FOR 2015
£25,000-£27,000

UNIVERSITY VISITS IN 2014-15
*Please check with your university careers
service for full details of local events.*

MINIMUM ENTRY REQUIREMENTS
2.2 Degree

APPLICATION DEADLINE
3rd November 2014
*The deadline for the Commercial &
Finance and Analytical programmes
is 30th September 2014.*

FURTHER INFORMATION
www.Top100GraduateEmployers.com
*Register now for the latest news, events
information and graduate recruitment
details for Britain's leading employers.*

**The Fast Stream is an unrivalled opportunity to lead changes
that count and build a career that matters. At the heart of
government, Fast Streamers work on some of the most vital and
challenging issues facing Britain now and in the future. With a
diversity of roles offering incredible professional development.**

The Fast Stream is an accelerated learning and development programme for
graduates with the motivation and the potential to become the future leaders
of the Civil Service. Fast Streamers are given considerable responsibility from
the outset: they are stretched and challenged on a daily basis, and they move
regularly between posts to gain a wide range of contrasting experiences and
build up an impressive portfolio of skills and knowledge.

Work ranges across professional areas including digital, communications,
policy development, corporate services, people management, commercial
awareness, financial management and project management, giving Fast
Streamers a wide understanding of how government delivers public services.
Comprehensive training and development combined with on-the-job learning
and support is provided. Successful applicants will receive an excellent package
of benefits.

There's no such thing as a typical Fast Streamer, and graduates from widely
diverse backgrounds are excited by the idea of making a positive and highly
visible impact on the most important and exciting issues facing the country.
Society is best served by a Civil Service which is as diverse as itself.

There are opportunities available across the UK in all areas of government,
offering graduates a unique perspective of work at the heart of current affairs
and key government agendas. There's no limit to where they could lead on the
Civil Service Fast Stream. All degree disciplines are welcome.

'Where will you lead?

Education. Health. Justice. Employment. Defence. Transport. Climate change. International development. Foreign affairs. If the government has a policy on something, it is guaranteed that Fast Streamers are working at the heart of it, putting their brains and their skills at the disposal of the whole of society.

The Civil Service Fast Stream offers the kind of leadership training you simply can't have anywhere else. Choose from an exciting range of generalist and specialist streams with a programme that's ranked among the top ten of The Times Top 100 Graduate Employers.

Learn more: faststream.civilservice.gov.uk

Civil Service
Fast Stream

CLIFFORD CHANCE

www.cliffordchance.com/gradsuk

graduate.recruitment@cliffordchance.com ✉

twitter.com/CCGradsUK 🐦   facebook.com/CliffordChanceGrads 🇫

youtube.com/CliffordChanceGrads ▶   linkedin.com/company/clifford-chance-llp/careers 🔗

Every year Clifford Chance looks for individuals who share the firm's ambition to remain right at the forefront of international law firms. Graduates who join Clifford Chance will become part of a team dedicated to tackling some of the most complex and fascinating legal issues facing the world today.

Clifford Chance works both internationally and domestically with a full range of clients, from multi-national and domestic corporates to financial institutions, regulatory authorities, supranational bodies, governments and government agencies. This is a firm where day-to-day work is often 'game-changing', and where trainees work on transformational deals and issues.

Clifford Chance is regularly singled out for the quality of its client service and legal expertise. Recent accolades include: No.1 International Law Firm in the Chambers Global 'Top 30' 2014; International Law Firm of the Year 2014 (IFLR Europe Awards); International Firm of the Year 2014 (Asian Legal Business Awards); Graduate Employer of the Year 2014 (National Graduate Recruitment Awards); Private Equity Team of the Year 2014 (Legal Business Awards) and Banking & Finance Law Firm of the Year 2014 (Chambers Global Awards).

The firm prides itself on bringing together exceptional lawyers from a wide range of backgrounds. This diversity stems from a firmly-held belief that different thinking translates into a competitive edge for clients. For that reason, Clifford Chance looks for graduates with drive and potential rather than a particular degree. Trainees will work hard. Focus and dedication are essential, but in return they receive all the investment and support needed to forge a compelling career.

GRADUATE VACANCIES IN 2015

LAW

NUMBER OF VACANCIES
100 graduate jobs
For training contracts starting in 2017.

LOCATIONS OF VACANCIES

STARTING SALARY FOR 2015
£40,500

UNIVERSITY VISITS IN 2014-15
ABERDEEN, BATH, BELFAST, BIRMINGHAM, BRISTOL, CAMBRIDGE, CARDIFF, CITY, DURHAM, EAST ANGLIA, EDINBURGH, EXETER, GLASGOW, KING'S COLLEGE LONDON, KENT, LANCASTER, LEEDS, LEICESTER, LONDON SCHOOL OF ECONOMICS, MANCHESTER, NEWCASTLE, NOTTINGHAM, OXFORD, QUEEN MARY LONDON, READING, SHEFFIELD, SOUTHAMPTON, ST ANDREWS, TRINITY COLLEGE DUBLIN, UNIVERSITY COLLEGE DUBLIN, UNIVERSITY COLLEGE LONDON, WARWICK, YORK
Please check with your university careers service for full details of local events.

MINIMUM ENTRY REQUIREMENTS
2.1 Degree
340 UCAS points

APPLICATION DEADLINE
Law: 30th June 2015
Non-law: 31st January 2015

FURTHER INFORMATION
www.Top100GraduateEmployers.com
Register now for the latest news, events information and graduate recruitment details for Britain's leading employers.

WORK ON BILLION-DOLLAR, MULTI-JURISDICTIONAL DEALS. JOIN A FIRM THAT'S FAMOUS FOR DOING WHAT'S NEVER BEEN DONE BEFORE. BECOME PART OF A GLOBAL ELITE. TOGETHER WE ARE CLIFFORD CHANCE.

When you start your career in law at Clifford Chance, you become part of something. We share an ambition that has fuelled our growth around the world – and our ability to tackle some of the most complex and fascinating legal issues facing the world today. As a trainee, you'll be an integral member of the team shaping those deals. You'll work hard. You'll push yourself. You'll feel the rewards. Because it may be our goals that unite us, but it's our diversity of talent that sets us apart.

CLIFFORD
CHANCE

CREDIT SUISSE

www.credit-suisse.com/careers

linkedin.com/company/credit-suisse **in**   facebook.com/creditsuissecareers **f**

the
future
at work

Credit Suisse is a global financial services company providing a broad range of advisory services, comprehensive solutions and excellent products through two global divisions, Private Banking & Wealth Management and Investment Banking. It serves companies, institutions and private clients around the world.

As a stable company with a long banking tradition, Credit Suisse is one of the most respected banks in the world, recognised by industry publications for its continued excellence and leading position in many key markets around the world.

Credit Suisse is active in more than 50 countries and employs over 46,000 people. Since its founding in 1856, the organisation has continuously set new standards in service and advice, and created intelligent solutions in response to changing client needs. It is renowned for its expertise and valued for its advice, innovation and execution.

Credit Suisse offers entry-level programmes in a variety of business areas. The organisation's programs give graduates the chance to make a difference from day one, and provide world-class training and support to help them to develop into future business leaders. Whichever programme successful candidates choose, they'll contribute to projects that have a significant impact on the business, while building their own expertise. And throughout their career with the company, graduates will benefit from cross-business and international mobility opportunities.

Credit Suisse looks for people with a wide range of experiences, interests and degrees who will add fresh perspectives to the business. The organisation's vision is to become the world's most admired bank. A graduate career with Credit Suisse can help shape the future of the organisation.

GRADUATE VACANCIES IN 2015
FINANCE
INVESTMENT BANKING
IT
SALES

NUMBER OF VACANCIES
150+ graduate jobs

LOCATIONS OF VACANCIES

Vacancies also available in Europe.

STARTING SALARY FOR 2015
£Competitive

UNIVERSITY VISITS IN 2014-15
BIRMINGHAM, BRISTOL, CAMBRIDGE, DURHAM, IMPERIAL COLLEGE LONDON, KING'S COLLEGE LONDON, LONDON SCHOOL OF ECONOMICS, MANCHESTER, NEWCASTLE, NOTTINGHAM, OXFORD, SOUTHAMPTON, UNIVERSITY COLLEGE LONDON, WARWICK
Please check with your university careers service for full details of local events.

MINIMUM ENTRY REQUIREMENTS
2.1 Degree

APPLICATION DEADLINE
Varies by function

FURTHER INFORMATION
www.Top100GraduateEmployers.com
Register now for the latest news, events information and graduate recruitment details for Britain's leading employers.

Deloitte.

With more and more projects focused on technology and the latest digital developments, world-leading professional services firm Deloitte approaches every client with a clear eye on the future. This vision enables them to advise big businesses on big decisions, tackle complex operations, and drive innovation.

What's more, the firm's advisory expertise is as broad as it is deep, extending to entire sectors and industries, from travel to retail, entertainment, government, charities and life sciences, to name just a few.

That focus extends to the firm's people, too. Those joining in Audit, Tax, Consulting, Corporate Finance or Technology will be exposed to a range of business areas and gain experience of inspiring, interesting work. They'll also receive expert training and support from some of the best minds in the business, helping them to build an enviable career.

With 23 offices throughout the UK, Deloitte offer a range of opportunities for students. They could join the graduate scheme and work towards a professional qualification while building on their technical and business skills. They could also choose to join one of Deloitte's work experience schemes (available in both spring and summer), or the industrial placement programme.

Deciding where to start a career is one of the biggest investments that a student will ever make. Whether joining as a graduate or undergraduate, at Deloitte, they can be sure that the investment is worthwhile as they'll have both the range of opportunities and supportive culture to develop into the professional they have the potential to be, and in ways that might surpass even their own expectations.

Deloitte welcomes people from all backgrounds, and applications from any degree discipline.

GRADUATE VACANCIES IN 2015
ACCOUNTANCY
CONSULTING
FINANCE
IT
PROPERTY

NUMBER OF VACANCIES
1,200 graduate jobs

LOCATIONS OF VACANCIES

STARTING SALARY FOR 2015
£Competitive
Plus 25 days holiday, pension, life assurance, personal accident insurance and a free mobile phone.

UNIVERSITY VISITS IN 2014-15
ABERDEEN, ASTON, BATH, BELFAST, BIRMINGHAM, BRISTOL, CAMBRIDGE, CARDIFF, CITY, DUNDEE, DURHAM, EAST ANGLIA, EDINBURGH, EXETER, GLASGOW, HERIOT-WATT, HULL, IMPERIAL COLLEGE LONDON, KING'S COLLEGE LONDON, KENT, LANCASTER, LEEDS, LEICESTER, LIVERPOOL, LONDON SCHOOL OF ECONOMICS, LOUGHBOROUGH, MANCHESTER, NEWCASTLE, NORTHUMBRIA, NOTTINGHAM, NOTTINGHAM TRENT, OXFORD, OXFORD BROOKES, QUEEN MARY LONDON, READING, ROYAL HOLLOWAY LONDON, SCHOOL OF AFRICAN STUDIES, SHEFFIELD, SOUTHAMPTON, ST ANDREWS, STRATHCLYDE, SURREY, SUSSEX, ULSTER, UNIVERSITY COLLEGE LONDON, WARWICK, YORK
Please check with your university careers service for full details of local events.

MINIMUM ENTRY REQUIREMENTS
2.1 Degree
280-360 UCAS points

APPLICATION DEADLINE
Year-round recruitment
Early application advised.

FURTHER INFORMATION
www.Top100GraduateEmployers.com
Register now for the latest news, events information and graduate recruitment details for Britain's leading employers.

DIAGEO

GRADUATE VACANCIES IN 2015
ENGINEERING
FINANCE
HUMAN RESOURCES
MARKETING
SALES

NUMBER OF VACANCIES
50 graduate jobs

LOCATIONS OF VACANCIES

Vacancies also available in Europe.

STARTING SALARY FOR 2015
£Competitive

UNIVERSITY VISITS IN 2014-15
BATH, BELFAST, DURHAM, EDINBURGH,
IMPERIAL COLLEGE LONDON,
LOUGHBOROUGH, MANCHESTER, OXFORD,
TRINITY COLLEGE DUBLIN, UNIVERSITY
COLLEGE DUBLIN, WARWICK
*Please check with your university careers
service for full details of local events.*

MINIMUM ENTRY REQUIREMENTS
2.1 Degree
300 UCAS points

APPLICATION DEADLINE
Year-round recruitment
Early application advised.

FURTHER INFORMATION
www.Top100GraduateEmployers.com
*Register now for the latest news, events
information and graduate recruitment
details for Britain's leading employers.*

Diageo is the world's leading premium drinks business, with iconic brands including Guinness, Smirnoff, Captain Morgan and Johnnie Walker, and a company purpose to celebrate life, every day, everywhere. At the core of the company are its values; passionate about customers and consumers, freedom to succeed, proud of what we do, be the best and valuing each other.

With over 28,000 talented people working globally, Diageo considers its people its biggest asset. It creates an environment with the right values, ethics and opportunity for growth at every stage of its employees' careers. Graduates are provided with a platform to explore their curiosity and seek out new opportunities. Exceptional development programmes build their experience, enabling each graduate to become bigger and better leaders for the future.

Outstanding training and real challenges await all employees from day one, with support from dedicated buddies and mentors. Being a truly global company, with operations in over 180 countries, Diageo offers employees the opportunity to broaden their horizons.

As one might expect from a company founded by successful entrepreneurs, employees are encouraged to act like owners, with energy and passion, whether in Sales, Marketing or any other part of the business. Successful applicants to the three-year programme – and undergraduate summer internships – will be bright, curious and driven to make a difference.

Competitive salaries, great benefits, and a happy work-life balance are just part of the package. With many opportunities for employees to work on local or global community initiatives, it's no wonder Diageo is number 8 in the World's Best Place to work – Great Place to Work 2013 survey.

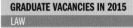
DLA Piper is a global law firm with 4,200 lawyers located in more than 30 countries throughout the Americas, Asia Pacific, Europe and the Middle East, positioning the firm to help companies with their legal needs anywhere in the world. In the UK, it provides legal advice from London and the other major centres.

Unlike many law firms, DLA Piper is organised to provide clients with a range of essential business advice, not just on large scale mergers and acquisitions and banking deals but also on people and employment, commercial dealings, litigation, insurance, real estate, IT, intellectual property, plans for restructuring and tax. It has a comprehensive, award winning client relationship management programme and the brand is built upon local legal excellence and global capability.

DLA Piper looks for opportunities to use its strength as a leading business law firm to make a positive contribution in their local and global communities. The firm's Corporate Responsibility initiatives demonstrate how their values are embedded in the way the firm engages with its people, its clients and its communities.

Within its trainee cohort the firm needs a diverse group of highly talented individuals who have a consistently strong academic performance, formidable commercial acumen, who are articulate, ambitious and driven with sharp minds, enthusiasm and intellectual curiosity. In return, DLA Piper offers a dynamic and diverse environment in which people can build a long and fruitful career and have their success rewarded.

Trainees complete four six-month seats and are given an opportunity to express what areas of law they would like to experience during their training contracts. They have the opportunity to do a seat abroad, or a client secondment.

GRADUATE VACANCIES IN 2015
LAW

NUMBER OF VACANCIES
80 graduate jobs
For training contracts starting in 2017.

LOCATIONS OF VACANCIES

STARTING SALARY FOR 2015
£23,000-£40,000

UNIVERSITY VISITS IN 2014-15
ABERDEEN, BIRMINGHAM, BRISTOL, CAMBRIDGE, CITY, DUNDEE, DURHAM, EDINBURGH, EXETER, GLASGOW, KING'S COLLEGE LONDON, LANCASTER, LEEDS, LIVERPOOL, LONDON SCHOOL OF ECONOMICS, MANCHESTER, NEWCASTLE, NOTTINGHAM, OXFORD, SHEFFIELD, UNIVERSITY COLLEGE LONDON, WARWICK, YORK
Please check with your university careers service for full details of local events.

MINIMUM ENTRY REQUIREMENTS
2.1 Degree

APPLICATION DEADLINE
Law: 31st July 2015
Non-law: 31st July 2015

FURTHER INFORMATION
www.Top100GraduateEmployers.com
Register now for the latest news, events information and graduate recruitment details for Britain's leading employers.

BIGGER

OPPORTUNITIES

DLA Piper offers big opportunities to ambitious graduates – big firm, big clients, big careers.

Don't just take our word for it. Find out more at www.dlapipergraduates.co.uk

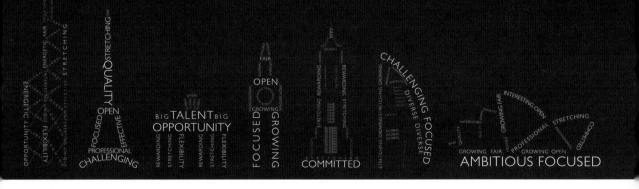

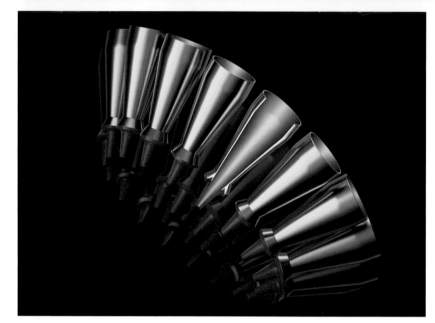

The world's first bagless vacuum. A hand dryer that doesn't use heat. A fan with no blades. For over 20 years, Dyson has been looking beyond the existing solutions to invent new technology. It's a philosophy this global, cutting-edge engineering firm calls 'wrong thinking'. And it's in the blood of every Dyson graduate.

It took rejection after rejection and more than 5,000 failed prototypes before James Dyson's cyclonic vacuum cleaner found success. But since going it alone to take on the big boys in 1993, Dyson vacuums now lead the market in the UK, Europe, Japan and the USA. More recently, they've developed a revolutionary new hand dryer and the world's first bladeless fan. But the ideas never stop. And to realise their ambitious future, Dyson are looking for grads with their own.

But there's no traditional graduate scheme at Dyson – they offer graduate jobs. So they will work on live global projects from the off. No fluff. No shadowing. No watching from the sidelines. And with the support to help them develop in a direction that suits their ambition, where they go – and how far – is up to them.

Dyson graduates will be joining over 3,000 engineers, scientists, marketing creatives, business development executives, web developers, financial analysts and more on the eve of the largest expansion in Dyson's history – with a £250m investment to double the size of their research and design HQ in Wiltshire, and a 25-year pipeline of exciting future technologies to develop.

Dyson doesn't look for a particular type of degree or experience. And they don't just recruit engineers – there's a lot going on outside the labs too. They want intelligent, articulate minds with the right attitude. People with a passion for technology. People who go beyond the job description. People who demonstrate the same qualities that drove James Dyson to carry on through all those prototypes and rejections – perseverance, perfectionism and wrong thinking.

GRADUATE VACANCIES IN 2015
ACCOUNTANCY
ENGINEERING
MARKETING
RESEARCH & DEVELOPMENT

NUMBER OF VACANCIES
70+ graduate jobs

LOCATIONS OF VACANCIES

STARTING SALARY FOR 2015
£22,000-£26,000
Plus a £2,000 sign-on bonus for engineers.

UNIVERSITY VISITS IN 2014-15
BATH, BRISTOL, BRUNEL, CAMBRIDGE, CARDIFF, IMPERIAL COLLEGE LONDON, LOUGHBOROUGH, MANCHESTER, NOTTINGHAM, OXFORD, SHEFFIELD, SOUTHAMPTON, TRINITY COLLEGE DUBLIN, UNIVERSITY COLLEGE LONDON
Please check with your university careers service for full details of local events.

MINIMUM ENTRY REQUIREMENTS
2.1 Degree

APPLICATION DEADLINE
Year-round recruitment
Early application advised.

FURTHER INFORMATION
www.Top100GraduateEmployers.com
Register now for the latest news, events information and graduate recruitment details for Britain's leading employers.

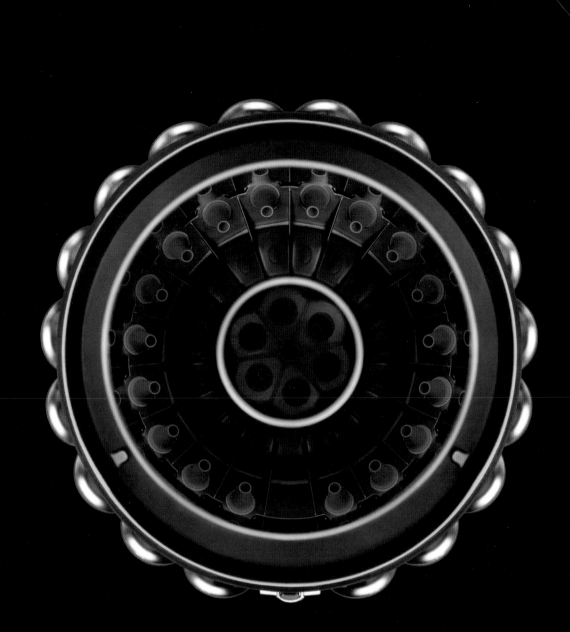

FAILURES WANTED.

We made over 2,000 prototypes when developing our latest vacuum.
That's over 2,000 machines that weren't quite right, and then just one that was.
But that's how we do things at Dyson. We relish failures. Each one pushes us on
to try something new. Every mistake leads to an improvement – and ultimately,
an invention. If you're bold enough to get things wrong, apply here:

www.careers.dyson.com

dyson

E.ON is a leading energy company. Five million homes and businesses rely on the firm for their electricity and gas each day. Part of the E.ON Group, it employs 12,000 people in the UK and more than 79,000 worldwide. To meet the growing demand for energy, it continually seeks the best graduate talent.

The company's vision is to become a trusted energy partner for its customers. To do this, E.ON is making energy both cleaner and simpler. On the one hand, it's improving its gas, coal and oil-fired power stations and producing more energy from renewable sources. On the other, it's talking to customers to find out what they want – introducing things like clear bills and fewer tariffs that are easier to understand.

E.ON's graduate schemes have been specifically designed to develop its future leaders. The company offers nine schemes in all, lasting from 18-24 months. Together, they cover a wide range of areas, from engineering and finance to HR and marketing. Wherever they join, graduates get a good view of the overall business – both in the UK and abroad. They also get an inside look at the people, processes and technology that are transforming energy today.

Support and choice are at the heart of all E.ON's graduate schemes. From day one, each graduate will be assigned a mentor, who'll help them create their own personal development plan – and put it into action. They'll also be able to attend a series of professional workshops, based on their skills and aspirations. Last but not least, they'll also receive time and funding to work towards whatever qualifications they need to develop their career – from Chartered status for engineers to the CIPD for HR professionals. E.ON sees graduates as integral to its future. So from the outset, each graduate can expect a significant investment in their training and development – plus plenty of real world challenges.

GRADUATE VACANCIES IN 2015
ENGINEERING
FINANCE
GENERAL MANAGEMENT
HUMAN RESOURCES
IT
MARKETING
SALES

NUMBER OF VACANCIES
45-50 graduate jobs

LOCATIONS OF VACANCIES

STARTING SALARY FOR 2015
£27,500-£40,000
Plus a £1,500 welcome bonus.

UNIVERSITY VISITS IN 2014-15
ASTON, BATH, BIRMINGHAM, DURHAM,
LANCASTER, LEEDS, LEICESTER,
LOUGHBOROUGH, MANCHESTER,
NOTTINGHAM, NOTTINGHAM TRENT,
SHEFFIELD, WARWICK
Please check with your university careers service for full details of local events.

MINIMUM ENTRY REQUIREMENTS
2.1 Degree

APPLICATION DEADLINE
30th November 2014

FURTHER INFORMATION
www.Top100GraduateEmployers.com
Register now for the latest news, events information and graduate recruitment details for Britain's leading employers.

Harnessing the insights of the industry's biggest influencers

If not you, then who?

Environmental policies matter when you're an energy company. So it's important that ours are based on robust research and the latest thinking. As a first assignment, we asked one of our graduates to investigate the environmental dimension of offshore wind. They collated insights from influential people from all over the scientific community, distilling their findings in a report. This report now forms a key pillar for one of our environmental policies — and it's just one example of how E.ON graduates have a great influence.

Find out more about our diverse range of programmes at eonenergy.com/graduates

Helping our customers.
We're on it.

eDF ENERGY

EDF Energy wants to make energy better: fairer, simpler, cleaner and more affordable. As the largest generator of low-carbon electricity in the UK, they're perfectly placed to tackle some of the energy industry's greatest challenges, including climate change and security of supply.

EDF Energy's graduates will help to make a sustainable energy a reality. By harnessing the potential of nuclear power, they'll play an important part in defining the UK energy industry for generations to come. From the technical challenges of building and maintaining nuclear power stations to the commercial, logistical and human aspects of managing a fast-growing and rapidly changing business, few organisations offer the scale or scope of opportunity.

EDF Energy's graduate programmes are designed to support, test and develop people who have the potential to be future industry leaders. Technically challenging, professionally inspiring and personally rewarding, all programmes offer intensive training matched by real challenges and responsibility from day one. And, with careers in civil, electrical, mechanical, materials and chemical engineering; physics, chemistry, mathematics and environmental science; finance, HR, supply chain, sustainability and energy analysis, EDF Energy has something to suit graduates from almost every degree discipline.

This is work that graduates can feel good about – and they'll feel good doing it too, in a working culture that's committed to being more inclusive, more diverse and more empowering. What's more, the benefits package is designed to match individual talents and reward contribution to the business.

Committed to reducing the intensity of CO_2 emissions from electricity production to 60% and helping the UK meet its target of 80% reductions in CO_2 by 2050, EDF Energy offers graduates a feel-good challenge like no other.

GRADUATE VACANCIES IN 2015

ENGINEERING
FINANCE
GENERAL MANAGEMENT
HUMAN RESOURCES

NUMBER OF VACANCIES
Around 60 graduate jobs

LOCATIONS OF VACANCIES

STARTING SALARY FOR 2015
£Competitive
2015 Pay Award pending.

UNIVERSITY VISITS IN 2014-15
BIRMINGHAM, BRISTOL, CAMBRIDGE, IMPERIAL COLLEGE LONDON, LEICESTER, LOUGHBOROUGH, MANCHESTER, OXFORD, STRATHCLYDE, UNIVERSITY COLLEGE LONDON
Please check with your university careers service for full details of local events.

MINIMUM ENTRY REQUIREMENTS
2.1 Degree
Relevant degree required for some roles.

APPLICATION DEADLINE
January 2015

FURTHER INFORMATION
www.Top100GraduateEmployers.com
Register now for the latest news, events information and graduate recruitment details for Britain's leading employers.

YOU'LL DISCOVER YOUR PATH. TOGETHER WE'LL MAKE ENERGY BETTER.

Exceptional opportunities for graduates from all disciplines.

It's time to make a difference and feel good about it. To apply fresh thinking and see your ideas in action. To define the UK energy industry for generations to come. Perhaps you're up for the engineering challenge of building our nuclear future. Or maybe the commercial, logistical and human aspects of managing a fast-growing business are more your thing. Whichever route you choose, expect a rewarding journey with EDF Energy.

Find out more at **edfenergy.com/graduates**

eDF
ENERGY

Looking for a challenging career in a dynamic environment? Based in the heart of Europe, the EU Institutions offer a truly international career to ambitious and capable graduates. Serving 500 million citizens, a range of options are available, all with the chance to make a real and lasting difference.

For final-year students and graduates, entry-level positions are available in various fields, from law to economics or languages, as well as more general policy or project management roles. New recruits could be drafting legislation, helping to implement EU law, developing communication strategies, or managing projects and resources.

Most positions are based either in Brussels or Luxembourg, with around 20% of staff based in offices throughout the world. Applying for an EU Career could in practice mean working for the European Commission, Council of the EU, European Parliament, European External Action Service, European Court of Justice, European Court of Auditors, as well as other EU bodies and agencies or any of the other main EU Institutions or Agencies.

Interested applicants will need to prove their strong analytical, organisational and communication skills, a drive to deliver the best possible results, the ability to work effectively as part of a multi-cultural team, and a potential for leadership and personal development.

Candidates are selected through a process of open competition, which generally consists of a first round of computer-based tests in centres throughout the EU, followed by an assessment centre in Brussels or Luxembourg for the best performers. The main graduate recruitment cycle normally opens in the spring, but all of the EU Institutions offer paid graduate traineeships throughout the year – a great way to gain a first taste of a future EU career.

GRADUATE VACANCIES IN 2015
- FINANCE
- GENERAL MANAGEMENT
- HUMAN RESOURCES
- IT
- LAW
- MARKETING
- MEDIA
- RESEARCH & DEVELOPMENT

NUMBER OF VACANCIES
No fixed quota

LOCATIONS OF VACANCIES

Vacancies available in Europe.

STARTING SALARY FOR 2015
£41,500+

UNIVERSITY VISITS IN 2014-15
ABERYSTWYTH, BATH, BELFAST, BRISTOL, CAMBRIDGE, CARDIFF, DURHAM, EAST ANGLIA, EDINBURGH, EXETER, KING'S COLLEGE LONDON, KENT, LEEDS, LEICESTER, LIVERPOOL, MANCHESTER, NEWCASTLE, OXFORD, SHEFFIELD, SOUTHAMPTON, ST ANDREWS, STRATHCLYDE, SURREY, SUSSEX, TRINITY COLLEGE DUBLIN, UNIVERSITY COLLEGE DUBLIN, UNIVERSITY COLLEGE LONDON, WARWICK, YORK
Please check with your university careers service for full details of local events.

MINIMUM ENTRY REQUIREMENTS
Relevant degree required for some roles.

APPLICATION DEADLINE
Varies by function

FURTHER INFORMATION
www.Top100GraduateEmployers.com
Register now for the latest news, events information and graduate recruitment details for Britain's leading employers.

FACE A BIGGER CHALLENGE

"What I really love about my job is that I'm working right at the heart of international politics and at the top of the news agenda. One day I might be live tweeting from a European Council summit or the G7, and the next working on the Council's long-term social media strategy or advising upcoming Council presidencies on their social media activities.

"I get to travel a lot, speak different languages, and meet new people from all over the world. But what I really appreciate is how the EU institutions invest in their staff, and the opportunities to build my career through new skills and experiences."

Alexandra coordinates social media for the Council of the European Union. She studied History.

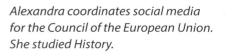

eu careers

eu-careers.eu

ExxonMobil

GRADUATE VACANCIES IN 2015
ENGINEERING
FINANCE
HUMAN RESOURCES
IT
MARKETING
SALES

NUMBER OF VACANCIES
No fixed quota

LOCATIONS OF VACANCIES

Imagine working for the world's largest publicly traded oil and gas company, on tasks that affect nearly everyone in the world today and for future generations to come. ExxonMobil in the UK is better known for its Esso and Mobil brands due to the success of its service stations and high performance lubricants.

ExxonMobil offers challenging long-term careers to high performing graduates, as well as summer and year placements with real responsibility!

There's no such thing as an average day at ExxonMobil and there are many different career paths available from a technical career to a leadership position to a commercial role. For graduates who are looking for a long-term career that will be challenging, rewarding and certainly varied, then a career with ExxonMobil might just be for them.

What are ExxonMobil looking for? For the technical schemes, applications are welcomed from Chemical, Electrical and Mechanical Engineers with a 2:1 minimum. For the commercial schemes, applications from a number of disciplines including Science/Engineering/IT/Business degrees with a 2:1 minimum are accepted.

In addition to the competitive base salary, acceptance bursary, relocation allowance and first month's accommodation being provided, employees are also offered matched 2-for-1 Share Scheme, final salary pension plan, Private Health Care Scheme, 33 days holiday pro rata including public holidays, £1,500 interest-free loan, free sports facilities, subsidised dining facilities at some locations, voluntary community activities, tailored graduate training and continuous development, support towards studying for professional qualifications such as CIMA and IChemE, international opportunities and job rotations every two to three years with opportunities to develop and hone skills.

STARTING SALARY FOR 2015
£38,000+
Plus a £1,000 acceptance bursary, £2,500 relocation allowance and the first month's accommodation is provided.

UNIVERSITY VISITS IN 2014-15
BATH, BIRMINGHAM, CAMBRIDGE, EDINBURGH, IMPERIAL COLLEGE LONDON, KING'S COLLEGE LONDON, LOUGHBOROUGH, MANCHESTER, NEWCASTLE, NORTHUMBRIA, NOTTINGHAM, SOUTHAMPTON, STRATHCLYDE, SURREY, UNIVERSITY COLLEGE LONDON
Please check with your university careers service for full details of local events.

MINIMUM ENTRY REQUIREMENTS
2.1 Degree
Relevant degree required for some roles.

APPLICATION DEADLINE
Varies by function

FURTHER INFORMATION
www.Top100GraduateEmployers.com
Register now for the latest news, events information and graduate recruitment details for Britain's leading employers.

EY
Building a better working world

GRADUATE VACANCIES IN 2015

ACCOUNTANCY

CONSULTING

FINANCE

IT

NUMBER OF VACANCIES
800 graduate jobs

LOCATIONS OF VACANCIES

Vacancies also available in Europe.

STARTING SALARY FOR 2015
£Competitive

UNIVERSITY VISITS IN 2014-15
ABERDEEN, ASTON, BATH, BIRMINGHAM, BRISTOL, CAMBRIDGE, CARDIFF, CITY, DURHAM, EDINBURGH, EXETER, GLASGOW, IMPERIAL COLLEGE LONDON, KING'S COLLEGE LONDON, LANCASTER, LEEDS, LONDON SCHOOL OF ECONOMICS, LOUGHBOROUGH, MANCHESTER, NEWCASTLE, OXFORD, READING, SHEFFIELD, SOUTHAMPTON, ST ANDREWS, STRATHCLYDE, SURREY, UNIVERSITY COLLEGE LONDON, WARWICK, YORK
Please check with your university careers service for full details of local events.

MINIMUM ENTRY REQUIREMENTS
2.1 Degree
300 UCAS points

APPLICATION DEADLINE
Year-round recruitment

FURTHER INFORMATION
www.Top100GraduateEmployers.com
Register now for the latest news, events information and graduate recruitment details for Britain's leading employers.

EY is one of the world's leading professional services organisations. It has 190,000 people working across 150 countries and together generates revenues of more than US $25.8 billion. By 2020 they plan to be a $50 billion organisation. It seeks driven, ambitious graduates who are looking for a stimulating and challenging start to their business career.

EY's clients include some of the most successful, innovative and respected global organisations, and range across all industry and public sectors. EY's people understand how businesses work and it is their ingenuity, dynamism and creativity that help anticipate and meet their clients' needs: improving how they work, grow, seize opportunities, and make vital business decisions – they help build trust and confidence in economies the world over.

EY prides itself on its world-class training, mentoring and professional qualifications – the first step to a successful, varied and fulfilling career path. The firm offers on-campus workshops with key advice on the graduate job application process, as well as providing useful insights on how to increase employability and hone the skills students need to get ahead in their careers. Inspiring talks offer insights into the business world and open debates on how organisations work with EY to combat complex business issues, helping students with their commercial awareness.

Students will work with leading industry experts, building a network within EY and beyond, and have the opportunity to hone the skills and expertise necessary for an exciting career. A graduate's ambition will determine how far they go.

The exceptional EY experience will last a lifetime. Careers at the top of the business world are often defined by where they start. At EY, the skills, contacts, experiences and perspective gained will give students the advantage.

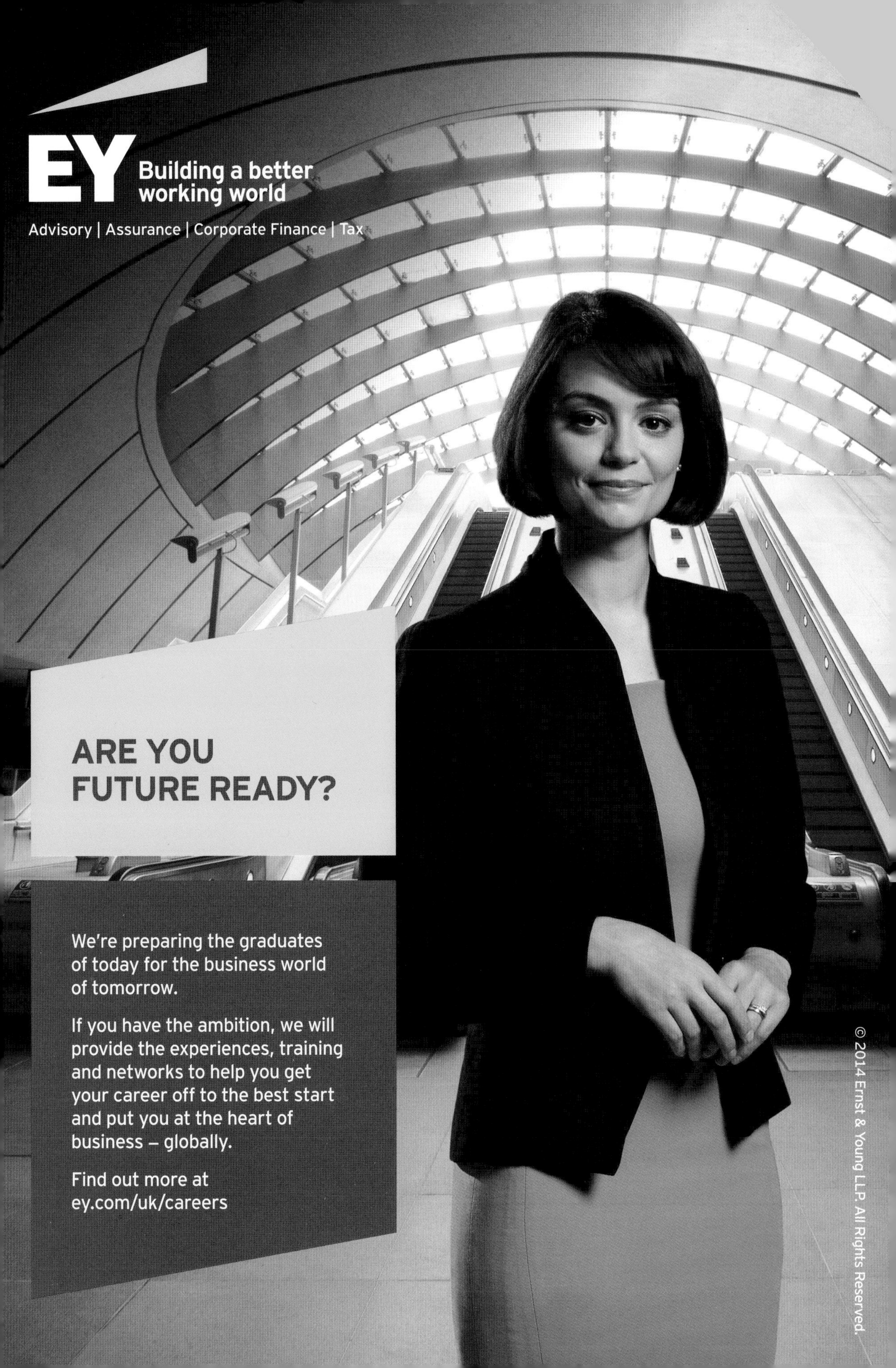
EY
Building a better working world
Advisory | Assurance | Corporate Finance | Tax
ARE YOU FUTURE READY?
We're preparing the graduates of today for the business world of tomorrow.
If you have the ambition, we will provide the experiences, training and networks to help you get your career off to the best start and put you at the heart of business – globally.
Find out more at ey.com/uk/careers
© 2014 Ernst & Young LLP. All Rights Reserved.

Foreign &
Commonwealth
Office

GRADUATE VACANCIES IN 2015

FINANCE
GENERAL MANAGEMENT
HUMAN RESOURCES
LOGISTICS
MEDIA
RESEARCH & DEVELOPMENT

NUMBER OF VACANCIES
Around 35 graduate jobs

LOCATIONS OF VACANCIES

A career in the Diplomatic Service isn't just a career – it's an opportunity to promote Britain and its interests in a changing world, to gain an unrivalled international perspective on domestic and global issues, to work with other countries through foreign policy, and to be part of a government department that prioritises people, both at home and abroad.

Most people working in the Diplomatic Service change job roles every 3-4 years so, as graduates progress through their careers with the Foreign and Commonwealth Office (FCO), they could be involved with everything from countering international terrorism to promoting a low-carbon economy, from managing migration to handling foreign crises.

All graduates will contribute to the FCO's three main goals: to keep Britain safe by counteracting and defeating terrorism that threatens the UK at its source, preventing nuclear proliferation and protecting the British people and economy; to make Britain prosperous by looking beyond UK borders to promote growth and jobs at home pursuing export, investment and trade and; to support British nationals overseas, by having the expert local knowledge and linguistics skills that British nationals require in times of distress.

No two days are the same and graduates with the willingness to learn and improve will be challenged to reach their full potential; those coming into the FCO through the Diplomatic Fast Stream will have the opportunity to take job postings both in London and overseas.

The FCO welcomes applicants from all backgrounds, and graduates don't need specific experience or degree subjects; successful applicants require core, transferrable abilities such as making effective decisions, leading and communicating, and collaborating and partnering.

STARTING SALARY FOR 2015
Around £27,000
All staff also receive a competitive rewards package.

UNIVERSITY VISITS IN 2014-15
ASTON, BATH, BIRMINGHAM, BRADFORD, BRISTOL, CAMBRIDGE, CARDIFF, EDINBURGH, EXETER, GLASGOW, KING'S COLLEGE LONDON, LEEDS, LIVERPOOL, LONDON SCHOOL OF ECONOMICS, MANCHESTER, NOTTINGHAM, OXFORD, QUEEN MARY LONDON, ROYAL HOLLOWAY LONDON, SCHOOL OF AFRICAN STUDIES, SHEFFIELD, SOUTHAMPTON, SURREY, UNIVERSITY COLLEGE LONDON
Please check with your university careers service for full details of local events.

MINIMUM ENTRY REQUIREMENTS
2.2 Degree

APPLICATION DEADLINE
31st October 2014

FURTHER INFORMATION
www.Top100GraduateEmployers.com
Register now for the latest news, events information and graduate recruitment details for Britain's leading employers.

A global network

Promoting British interests overseas, safeguarding Britain's security and supporting our citizens and businesses from 270 diplomatic posts in 160 countries around the world.

The FCO aims to recruit a talented and diverse workforce which reflects the society we serve.

We actively seek applications from all sections of society and offer positions to suitably qualified individuals regardless of ethnicity, social or educational background, age, disability or sexual orientation, with all appointments and future promotions made on individual merit.

For information about current opportunities:

http://tinyurl.com/**fco-careers**

@fcocareers

Freshfields

As an international law firm, Freshfields Bruckhaus Deringer advises some of the world's most well-known businesses. For graduates keen to pursue a career in commercial law, the firm offers challenging work that demands a strong intellect and a desire to help ambitious businesses achieve long-term success.

The firm provides clients with a global service from its network of offices across Europe, the US, the Middle East and Asia. It is essential that this service is consistent and of the highest quality.

Graduates who accept a training contract with the firm have the opportunity to experience up to eight areas of law – twice the number offered by most law firms. The training is largely provided from the firm's London office but many trainees will also spend time on secondment to a client or to one of the firm's European, US, Middle Eastern or Asian offices.

The lawyers work in teams, often of no more than three: a partner, an associate and a trainee. Whatever clients want to achieve, the team's job is to work out how. Is it possible? What will be the most effective way of structuring the deal or tackling the problem? What are the risks? How should it be documented? The team has to provide real commercial solutions, not just what is right or wrong in law.

Background, university and degree studied are immaterial. But every successful candidate has three qualities that are non-negotiable: intellectual talent, excellent English (both written and verbal), and a generous spirit.

The firm pursues premium, cross-border work that is nearly always complicated. This means that the learning curve is steep, so the graduates who do best are those who like to be challenged.

GRADUATE VACANCIES IN 2015
LAW

NUMBER OF VACANCIES
80 graduate jobs
For training contracts starting in 2017.

LOCATIONS OF VACANCIES

STARTING SALARY FOR 2015
£40,500
Maintenance grants for GDL and LPC students.

UNIVERSITY VISITS IN 2014-15
ABERDEEN, BATH, BELFAST, BIRMINGHAM, BRISTOL, CAMBRIDGE, CARDIFF, CITY, DURHAM, EDINBURGH, EXETER, GLASGOW, KING'S COLLEGE LONDON, KENT, LANCASTER, LEEDS, LEICESTER, LIVERPOOL, LONDON SCHOOL OF ECONOMICS, MANCHESTER, NEWCASTLE, NOTTINGHAM, OXFORD, QUEEN MARY LONDON, READING, SCHOOL OF AFRICAN STUDIES, SHEFFIELD, SOUTHAMPTON, ST ANDREWS, TRINITY COLLEGE DUBLIN, UNIVERSITY COLLEGE DUBLIN, UNIVERSITY COLLEGE LONDON, WARWICK, YORK
Please check with your university careers service for full details of local events.

APPLICATION DEADLINE
Law: 31st July 2015
Non-law: 6th January 2015

FURTHER INFORMATION
www.Top100GraduateEmployers.com
Register now for the latest news, events information and graduate recruitment details for Britain's leading employers.

You've come too far to be ordinary

And now you've set your sights on a career in international commercial law

You want colleagues who are bright, friendly and fun to work with. And work that's interesting, complicated, intellectually challenging, high-value and international.

You want the best (and the broadest) training you can get. Training that's not run-of-the-mill. Training where you can explore up to eight areas of law — double that offered by other firms.

80 training contracts
8 seats
46 overseas secondments

Find out more at:

freshfields.com/uktrainees

@uktrainees

FreshfieldsUKTrainees

Freshfields

Nicole Shui
Trainee
Philosophy and
Economics, UCL

Nicole's story:
freshfields.com/
uktrainees/nicole

Freshfields Bruckhaus Deringer LLP

Freshfields

FRONTLINE

CHANGING LIVES

www.thefrontline.org.uk

recruitment@thefrontline.org.uk ✉

twitter.com/FrontlineSW 🐦 facebook.com/FrontlineChangingLives f

youtube.com/FrontlineSW ▶ linkedin.com/company/frontline-org in

There are lots of graduate programmes out there. Most involve nice, comfortable office jobs. Frontline is different. Participants work with families, schools, courts and the police to change lives. 99% would run in the opposite direction. But Frontline is seeking the 1% who really want to make a difference.

Frontline's two-year graduate programme is a new opportunity for exceptional individuals to join one of Britain's toughest and most rewarding professions. An innovative approach to social work training, this demanding programme places high achievers in child protection teams in Greater Manchester, Greater London, Essex and Buckinghamshire to transform lives.

The programme begins with a five-week summer residential where a team of world-leading academics and individuals with care experience provide participants with master classes in social work practice. In September, participants join a local authority and start the first year, learning 'on-the-job' in teams of four. They receive full-time supervision from an experienced social worker and ongoing academic input. Upon qualification, the second year consists of 12 months guaranteed employment as a children's social worker and the opportunity to study towards a Masters or systemic practice qualification.

An integral part of Frontline's approach is its focus on leadership. The best social workers have the leadership skills to bring together a wide range of agencies, establish a vision with a family and influence people to act accordingly. Frontline is committed to instilling these skills in participants so they can drive positive change both in social work and in broader society. Its leadership development programme, run in partnership with Deloitte, will give participants the confidence to drive change whatever their future career path.

Frontline accepts applications from any discipline each autumn.

GRADUATE VACANCIES IN 2015

GENERAL MANAGEMENT
HUMAN RESOURCES
LAW
RESEARCH & DEVELOPMENT

NUMBER OF VACANCIES
132 graduate jobs

LOCATIONS OF VACANCIES

STARTING SALARY FOR 2015
£Competitive

UNIVERSITY VISITS IN 2014-15
ASTON, BIRMINGHAM, BRISTOL, CAMBRIDGE, CARDIFF, DURHAM, EDINBURGH, KING'S COLLEGE LONDON, LANCASTER, LEEDS, LEICESTER, LIVERPOOL, LONDON SCHOOL OF ECONOMICS, LOUGHBOROUGH, MANCHESTER, NOTTINGHAM, OXFORD, READING, SHEFFIELD, SUSSEX, UNIVERSITY COLLEGE LONDON, WARWICK, YORK

Please check with your university careers service for full details of local events.

MINIMUM ENTRY REQUIREMENTS
2.1 Degree
300 UCAS points

APPLICATION DEADLINE
November 2014

FURTHER INFORMATION
www.Top100GraduateEmployers.com
Register now for the latest news, events information and graduate recruitment details for Britain's leading employers.

THE TOUGHEST JOB IN THE CITY. COMES WITH THE BIGGEST BONUS.

FRONTLINE

CHANGING LIVES

Frontline is a new initiative designed to recruit outstanding graduates to be leaders in social work and in broader society. Successful applicants will take part in an intensive and innovative two year leadership programme, and gain a masters degree. But most importantly, they'll be working to transform the lives of vulnerable children and young people.

Because there's no bigger bonus than changing a life for the better.

www.thefrontline.org.uk

do more
feel better
live longer

One of the world's leading healthcare companies, GSK gives its people the chance to answer some of the planet's biggest questions. Questions about future healthcare needs and about building an innovative, global business to meet them, as well as questions about their personal and professional growth.

Dedicated to helping millions of people around the world to do more, feel better and live longer, GSK is revolutionising its business to meet changing healthcare needs from London to Lima, Lusaka, Luzhou and Lahore. GSK invested £3.4 billion in R&D in 2013 and topped the Access to Medicine Index, underlining its commitment to tackle some of the world's deadliest diseases by embracing new, open and innovative ways of working.

GSK discover, develop, manufacture and distribute vaccines, prescription medicines and consumer health products. Based in the UK, with operations in over 150 countries, GSK produce a huge range of healthcare products from lifesaving prescription medicines and vaccines to popular consumer products like Maximuscle, Sensodyne, Aquafresh and Panadol. In fact, every year GSK screen about 65 million compounds, make over four billion packs of medicines and healthcare products, and supply one quarter of the world's vaccines.

GSK is deeply committed to developing people through a range of ongoing development opportunities that includes tailored, 2-3 year rotational graduate programmes and industrial or summer placements. So it offers graduates the trust and respect to be themselves, and develop their careers across an incredibly diverse collection of businesses and geographies, in an environment where personal growth can play a vital part in the changing face of the business.

Most of all, GSK graduates enjoy the sense of purpose that comes from leading change in an industry that touches millions every day.

GRADUATE VACANCIES IN 2015

ENGINEERING
FINANCE
HUMAN RESOURCES
IT
MARKETING
PURCHASING
RESEARCH & DEVELOPMENT
SALES

NUMBER OF VACANCIES
65+ graduate jobs

LOCATIONS OF VACANCIES

Vacancies also available in Europe, Asia, the USA and elsewhere in the world.

STARTING SALARY FOR 2015
£Competitive

UNIVERSITY VISITS IN 2014-15
ASTON, CAMBRIDGE, DURHAM, EDINBURGH, EXETER, IMPERIAL COLLEGE LONDON, LOUGHBOROUGH, MANCHESTER, NEWCASTLE, NOTTINGHAM, OXFORD, UNIVERSITY COLLEGE LONDON, WARWICK
Please check with your university careers service for full details of local events.

MINIMUM ENTRY REQUIREMENTS
2.1 Degree

APPLICATION DEADLINE
Year-round recruitment
Early application advised.

FURTHER INFORMATION
www.Top100GraduateEmployers.com
Register now for the latest news, events information and graduate recruitment details for Britain's leading employers.

do m...
feel bett...
live longer

Lead change.
Benefit millions of lives.

Join our Future Leaders Programme
and you'll be part of a leading
global business tackling the world's
biggest healthcare challenges. Bring
your curiosity. Share our ambition.
We'll give you the opportunities
to build the future you want.

Find out more at
www.futureleaders.gsk.com

Yazmin
IT Future Leaders Programme.
Ensuring leading IT systems
protect patient safety.

Goldman Sachs

It takes different academic backgrounds to make an impact.

Learn more at goldmansachs.com/careers in

The Goldman Sachs Group, Inc. is a leading global investment banking, securities and investment management firm that provides a wide range of financial services to a substantial and diversified client base that includes corporations, financial institutions, governments and high-net-worth individuals.

The people of Goldman Sachs share a passion for achieving results and recognise that success comes with integrity. Their unique backgrounds, individual perspectives and diverse skills are put to the test as they help the firm's clients achieve their business goals.

Goldman Sachs is structured in a series of divisions: Executive Office, Finance, Global Compliance, Global Investment Research, Human Capital Management, Internal Audit, Investment Banking, Investment Management, Legal, Merchant Banking, Operations, Securities, Services and Technology.

Nearly everyone – from the most senior leaders to junior analysts – is actively involved in recruiting as the goal is to recruit people who share the firm's core values. Academic achievement is important, but is only one indication of a person's potential.

Goldman Sachs recognises a diverse workforce encourages increased creativity and innovation. Diversity is crucial to improved performance and continued business success. To that end, the firm is committed to an environment that values diversity and promotes inclusion.

Academic discipline is less important to Goldman Sachs than the personal qualities an individual brings with them, however a strong interest in and appreciation of finance is important. Whatever the background may be, it is intellect, personality and zest for life that the company values the most.

GRADUATE VACANCIES IN 2015

ACCOUNTANCY

FINANCE

HUMAN RESOURCES

INVESTMENT BANKING

IT

NUMBER OF VACANCIES
300 graduate jobs

LOCATIONS OF VACANCIES

STARTING SALARY FOR 2015
£Competitive

UNIVERSITY VISITS IN 2014-15
BATH, BIRMINGHAM, BRISTOL, CAMBRIDGE, CITY, DURHAM, EDINBURGH, GLASGOW, IMPERIAL COLLEGE LONDON, KING'S COLLEGE LONDON, LONDON SCHOOL OF ECONOMICS, LOUGHBOROUGH, MANCHESTER, NOTTINGHAM, OXFORD, SOUTHAMPTON, TRINITY COLLEGE DUBLIN, UNIVERSITY COLLEGE DUBLIN, UNIVERSITY COLLEGE LONDON, WARWICK, YORK
Please check with your university careers service for full details of local events.

APPLICATION DEADLINE
2nd November 2014

FURTHER INFORMATION
www.Top100GraduateEmployers.com
Register now for the latest news, events information and graduate recruitment details for Britain's leading employers.

![Goldman Sachs]

HOW WILL YOU
MAKE AN IMPACT

CONTRIBUTE, COLLABORATE AND SUCCEED WITH A CAREER AT GOLDMAN SACHS

If you're the kind of person who can't wait to make a difference, consider a career at Goldman Sachs. We believe that good ideas and innovations can come from anyone, at any level. We offer meaningful opportunities, best-in-class training and a wide variety of career paths for talented people from all academic backgrounds. Plus, with access to important clients and projects, you'll have the chance to make an impact with global significance.

APPLICATION DEADLINES

NEW ANALYST: 2 November 2014
SUMMER PROGRAMME: 7 December 2014
SPRING PROGRAMME: 4 January 2015
WORK PLACEMENT PROGRAMME: 4 January 2015

 **DOWNLOAD OUR APP** to learn more about how you can make an impact.

goldmansachs.com/careers
in. 🖰 🐦 @GSCareers

Google™

Founders Larry Page and Sergey Brin met at Stanford University in 1995. By 1996, they had built a search engine that used links to determine the importance of individual web pages. Today, Google is a tech company that helps businesses of all kinds succeed on and off the web.

It's really the people that make Google the kind of company it is. Google hire people who are smart and determined, and favour ability over experience.

New grads joining Google will enter either the Small-to-Medium Business (SMB) Sales or Global Customer Services Teams. As small business experts, Googlers in SMB help to get local entrepreneurs on the map, and deliver a beautifully simple, intuitive experience that enables customers to grow their businesses. By spotting and analysing customer needs and trends, Google's innovative teams of strategists, account developers and customer support specialists work together on scalable solutions for each business, no matter its age or size.

Google hires graduates from all disciplines, from humanities and business related courses to engineering and computer science. The ideal candidate is someone who can demonstrate a passion for the online industry and someone who has made the most of their time at university through involvement in clubs, societies or relevant internships. Google hires graduates who have a variety of strengths and passions, not just isolated skill sets. For technical roles within engineering teams, specific skills will be required.

The Google Business Associate Programme is a two-year developmental programme that supplements a Googler's core role in SMB. It offers world-class training, equipping new joiners with the business, analytical and leadership skills needed to be successful at Google.

GRADUATE VACANCIES IN 2015

CONSULTING
ENGINEERING
HUMAN RESOURCES
IT
MARKETING
MEDIA
SALES

NUMBER OF VACANCIES
No fixed quota

LOCATIONS OF VACANCIES

Vacancies also available in Europe, Asia and the USA.

STARTING SALARY FOR 2015
£Competitive
Plus world-renowned perks and benefits.

UNIVERSITY VISITS IN 2014-15
Please check with your university careers service for full details of local events.

MINIMUM ENTRY REQUIREMENTS
2.1 Degree

APPLICATION DEADLINE
Year-round recruitment

FURTHER INFORMATION
www.Top100GraduateEmployers.com
Register now for the latest news, events information and graduate recruitment details for Britain's leading employers.

THE IDEA FOR GMAIL
BEGAN WITH  1 GOOGLER.

TODAY, IT HAS MORE THAN 425 MILLION USERS AND COUNTING.

DO COOL THINGS THAT MATTER

Google™

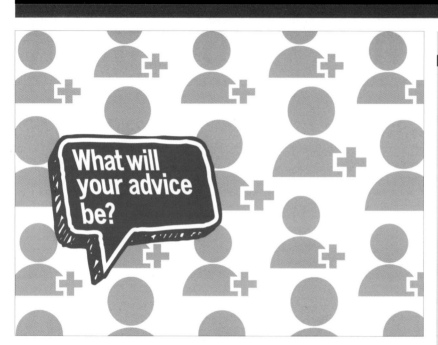

How to sum up a complex and exciting business like Grant Thornton? Simply put, they're part of a global organisation delivering audit, tax and advisory services to dynamic organisations in over 100 countries. In the UK alone, they deliver solutions to 40,000 clients, across a wide range of sectors.

Getting right to the core of client needs and meeting them with agility and insight is at the heart of their business. In today's competitive market, this blend of expertise and personal attention sets them apart.

Over 300 ambitious graduates, interns and placement students join Grant Thornton in over 20 of its 27 UK offices each year. They enjoy variety and responsibility from the start on exciting client assignments from multinationals to fast-growth companies such as start-ups. The learning curve is steep. Trainees can be leading their own team or portfolio by their second year. And with the firm's global reach there are plenty of opportunities for international exposure to clients and secondments.

The structured training, varied on-the-ground client experience and supportive working environment gives trainees the chance to develop and grow as trusted advisers with a deep understanding of business, as well as achieving a respected professional qualification and a competitive salary.

So who are they looking for? People with a passion for business, who combine technical thinking with their own instinct to give the kind of advice that makes a real difference to the organisations they work with. Grant Thornton's business advisers listen critically, dig deeper and have the confidence to challenge assumptions right from day one. They know it's about more than just the numbers, it's about enjoying tough challenges, seeking out opportunities and adding real value to clients by unlocking their potential for growth.

GRADUATE VACANCIES IN 2015
ACCOUNTANCY

NUMBER OF VACANCIES
300+ graduate jobs

LOCATIONS OF VACANCIES

STARTING SALARY FOR 2015
£Competitive

UNIVERSITY VISITS IN 2014-15
ASTON, BATH, BIRMINGHAM, BRISTOL, BRUNEL, CAMBRIDGE, CARDIFF, CITY, DURHAM, EAST ANGLIA, EDINBURGH, EXETER, GLASGOW, IMPERIAL COLLEGE LONDON, KING'S COLLEGE LONDON, LANCASTER, LEEDS, LEICESTER, LIVERPOOL, LONDON SCHOOL OF ECONOMICS, LOUGHBOROUGH, MANCHESTER, NEWCASTLE, NOTTINGHAM, OXFORD, READING, SHEFFIELD, SOUTHAMPTON, STRATHCLYDE, SURREY, SUSSEX, UNIVERSITY COLLEGE LONDON, WARWICK
Please check with your university careers service for full details of local events.

MINIMUM ENTRY REQUIREMENTS
Strong academic performance essential.

APPLICATION DEADLINE
Year-round recruitment
Early application advised.

FURTHER INFORMATION
www.Top100GraduateEmployers.com
Register now for the latest news, events information and graduate recruitment details for Britain's leading employers.

THINK TWICE BEFORE YOU FRIEND YOUR BOSS

What will your advice be?

Some advice just states the obvious. But to give the kind of advice that's going to make a real difference to your clients and your career, you've got to listen critically and be credible and confident enough to make suggestions right from day one. You'll enjoy tough challenges, seek out opportunities and be ready to kick start a career as a trusted business adviser working alongside our dynamic clients. Sound like you? Here's our advice: visit...

www.grant-thornton.co.uk/graduates

Grant Thornton

An instinct for growth™

HERBERT SMITH FREEHILLS

Herbert Smith Freehills is a global force with a market leading position in Asia Pacific. With 2,800 lawyers in offices spanning Asia, Australia, Europe, the Middle East and the US, the firm is the eighth largest law firm in the world and working across borders is at the heart of its philosophy.

The firm is committed to excellence, providing tailored legal advice of the highest quality to major corporations, governments, financial institutions and all types of commercial organisations.

Herbert Smith Freehills' disputes practice is acknowledged as the number one in the UK and Asia and includes the firm's leading international arbitration practice and award winning in-house advocacy unit, offering a complete litigation service and a realistic alternative to the bar. The firm is a market leader in corporate with a particular strength in the energy sector. Allied to this is a deep vein of quality that runs through its other practice areas including finance, competition, regulation and trade, real estate and employment, pensions and incentives. The firm also has specialist areas such as intellectual property and tax.

The training contract balances contentious and non-contentious work, pro bono opportunities, early responsibility and support. Trainees rotate around four six-month seats and are encouraged to go on secondment to a client or one of the firm's international offices.

Herbert Smith Freehills seeks to recruit people with the desire to be exceptional lawyers. As well as a solid academic record, applicants should have a strong level of commercial awareness and understand the importance of building relationships with clients and colleagues. The firm chooses people who are assured, perceptive, ambitious and empathetic. Combine these qualities with a creative and questioning mind and Herbert Smith Freehills will offer great challenges and rewards.

GRADUATE VACANCIES IN 2015

LAW

NUMBER OF VACANCIES
70 graduate jobs
For training contracts starting in 2017.

LOCATIONS OF VACANCIES

STARTING SALARY FOR 2015
£39,500
Plus full LPC and GDL fees and £6,000 maintenance grant (£5,000 if studying GDL outside London).

UNIVERSITY VISITS IN 2014-15
BELFAST, BIRMINGHAM, BRISTOL, CAMBRIDGE, CARDIFF, DURHAM, EDINBURGH, EXETER, GLASGOW, IMPERIAL COLLEGE LONDON, KING'S COLLEGE LONDON, LEEDS, LEICESTER, LONDON SCHOOL OF ECONOMICS, MANCHESTER, NEWCASTLE, NOTTINGHAM, OXFORD, QUEEN MARY LONDON, READING, SCHOOL OF AFRICAN STUDIES, SHEFFIELD, SOUTHAMPTON, ST ANDREWS, TRINITY COLLEGE DUBLIN, UNIVERSITY COLLEGE DUBLIN, UNIVERSITY COLLEGE LONDON, WARWICK, YORK
Please check with your university careers service for full details of local events.

MINIMUM ENTRY REQUIREMENTS
2.1 Degree

APPLICATION DEADLINE
Varies by function

FURTHER INFORMATION
www.Top100GraduateEmployers.com
Register now for the latest news, events information and graduate recruitment details for Britain's leading employers.

HERBERT SMITH FREEHILLS

BE AN EXCEPTIONAL LAWYER

What does it take to be an exceptional lawyer? It takes the curiosity to see what others can't, the ability to cut to the heart of the matter and the character to push further.

Whether you're from a law or non-law background, we offer training contracts with a first year starting salary of £39,500, first year workshops and vacation schemes. Our global network of offices provides exciting international opportunities for our trainees and vacation scheme students.

We see a fascinating future for the business of global law. If you do too, join us to meet our exceptional people and find out what life is really like at Herbert Smith Freehills.

70 TRAINING CONTRACTS

100 VACATION SCHEME PLACES

50 FIRST YEAR WORKSHOP PLACES

WWW.HERBERTSMITHFREEHILLS.COM/CAREERS/LONDON/GRADUATES

Hogan Lovells

Hogan Lovells is a top global law firm, with around 2,500 lawyers operating out of more than 40 offices in the United States, Europe, Latin America, Africa, the Middle East, and Asia. Their unique balance of ambition and approachability attracts prestigious clients and creates a working culture that ensures support and success for trainee solicitors.

Known for their global diversity and wide range of practice areas, Hogan Lovells has a strong reputation for corporate, finance, dispute resolution, government regulatory and intellectual property. This is also a firm that is recognised for their commitment to high quality training and development.

Each year they take on 60 trainee solicitors, composed of law and non-law graduates. The two-year training contract is split into four six-month periods of work experience known as 'seats'. Trainee solicitors move around four different practice areas during their two years here – gaining a range of experiences and spending time in either corporate or finance, as well as litigation. During the second year of the contract, they also offer options for secondment at their international offices and in-house with clients.

In addition to opportunities for trainee solicitors, Hogan Lovells makes up to 90 vacation scheme places available. These are split between their highly-regarded spring, summer and winter vacation schemes. Students will have the chance to work alongside partners, associates and trainees for up to three weeks – gaining insight into key practice areas such as corporate, finance and litigation. Vacation scheme students are exposed to real projects on a daily basis. They learn to draft documents, carry out legal research and co-ordinate meetings. There is even the opportunity to attend court. This hands-on learning is complemented by tailored workshops, discussions and social events.

GRADUATE VACANCIES IN 2015

LAW

NUMBER OF VACANCIES
60 graduate jobs
For training contracts starting in 2017.

LOCATIONS OF VACANCIES

STARTING SALARY FOR 2015
£39,500

UNIVERSITY VISITS IN 2014-15
BELFAST, BIRMINGHAM, BRISTOL, CAMBRIDGE, CARDIFF, DURHAM, EDINBURGH, EXETER, IMPERIAL COLLEGE LONDON, KING'S COLLEGE LONDON, LEEDS, LEICESTER, LONDON SCHOOL OF ECONOMICS, MANCHESTER, NEWCASTLE, NOTTINGHAM, OXFORD, SHEFFIELD, SOUTHAMPTON, ST ANDREWS, TRINITY COLLEGE DUBLIN, UNIVERSITY COLLEGE DUBLIN, UNIVERSITY COLLEGE LONDON, WARWICK, YORK
Please check with your university careers service for full details of local events.

MINIMUM ENTRY REQUIREMENTS
2.1 Degree

APPLICATION DEADLINE
Law: 31st July 2015
Non-law: 31st March 2015

FURTHER INFORMATION
www.Top100GraduateEmployers.com
Register now for the latest news, events information and graduate recruitment details for Britain's leading employers.

HSBC

GRADUATE VACANCIES IN 2015

FINANCE

INVESTMENT BANKING

SALES

NUMBER OF VACANCIES
300+ graduate jobs

LOCATIONS OF VACANCIES

Vacancies also available in Europe, Asia, the USA and elsewhere in the world.

STARTING SALARY FOR 2015
£Competitive

UNIVERSITY VISITS IN 2014-15
BATH, BIRMINGHAM, BRISTOL, CAMBRIDGE, CARDIFF, DURHAM, EXETER, GLASGOW, IMPERIAL COLLEGE LONDON, LEEDS, LEICESTER, LIVERPOOL, LONDON SCHOOL OF ECONOMICS, LOUGHBOROUGH, MANCHESTER, NEWCASTLE, NOTTINGHAM, OXFORD, SHEFFIELD, STRATHCLYDE, UNIVERSITY COLLEGE LONDON, WARWICK
Please check with your university careers service for full details of local events.

MINIMUM ENTRY REQUIREMENTS
2.1 Degree
300 UCAS points

APPLICATION DEADLINE
Varies by function

FURTHER INFORMATION
www.Top100GraduateEmployers.com
Register now for the latest news, events information and graduate recruitment details for Britain's leading employers.

HSBC is one of the world's largest banking and financial services organisations. HSBC have 263,000 people that operate in 75 countries and territories, serving a customer base of around 54 million customers. They aim to be where the growth is, connect customers to opportunities and enable businesses to thrive and economies prosper.

Once, banks were built for North American and European finance. But traditional economies have started to shift while new markets emerge and old ones slow down. The world is changing the way it does business – and where it does business. HSBC has always looked in new directions to create teams, resources and relationships. With a strong global network that reaches into emerging economies and established markets, HSBC is shaped for the future.

At HSBC, there's always room for difference, but everyone shares a focus on teamwork, a feeling of community and mutual respect. It's a culture focused on doing the right thing where people take responsibility for their actions.

By focusing on the long term, HSBC can build on its achievements; look for new opportunities and never lose sight of its heritage. People are proud to be part of an organisation that's always moving forward – and doing so responsibly. Now, HSBC want people who share a focus on the bigger picture and are ready for the global challenges and opportunities that they offer.

For graduates, that means there's a platform for talent that offers global experience and exposure to new markets. The challenges are real and graduates become integral members of a network that stretches around the world. At HSBC, graduates can see past their short term goals to build long and rewarding careers.

We see a future with so much to offer.
Do you?

Around the world, growth is bringing new prosperity; businesses are pioneering new trade routes; and new centres of wealth and influence are emerging. At HSBC, we're inspired by the ways the world is changing for our business and for our customers. That's why we're looking to connect with the best and the brightest people from across the globe. With so much to offer, we're ideally placed to help you realise your ambitions.

Achieve your potential at HSBC.
www.hsbc.com/careers

The world is changing, and it's innovative companies like IBM who are driving this transformation. At IBM, graduates will have limitless opportunities to do meaningful work using data and technology to make the world better and more efficient in an organisation full of passionate and dedicated individuals.

IBM work with some of the greatest and best known names on the planet, providing IT services and consultancy across all industries including retail, sport, business, finance, health, media and entertainment.

IBM look for the best and brightest graduates, from all universities, degree backgrounds and abilities. They want creative and passionate people who will share their dedication to tackling the world's toughest problems. Whether graduates want to pursue a career in consulting, technology, business, design or sales they'll have the chance to collaborate with extraordinary people in a creative environment to make the world work better.

IBM are dedicated to giving graduates every opportunity to enhance their career development. They'll work in an environment that cultivates creativity and individual differences, rewarding their best work.

IBM's award winning, bespoke training is designed to give graduates the personal, business and technical skills to take their career wherever they want to go. Graduates will continuously learn and develop new skills and have the opportunity to contribute to the enhancement of their field.

IBM will encourage graduates to extend their expertise through customised professional development and leadership training, allocating every graduate a professional development manager and a mentor to ensure graduates get the most out of the programme.

Be part of a global transformation and join IBM.

GRADUATE VACANCIES IN 2015

CONSULTING
IT
SALES

NUMBER OF VACANCIES
300+ graduate jobs

LOCATIONS OF VACANCIES

STARTING SALARY FOR 2015
£30,000+

UNIVERSITY VISITS IN 2014-15
ASTON, BATH, BIRMINGHAM, BRISTOL, CAMBRIDGE, CARDIFF, DURHAM, EDINBURGH, EXETER, GLASGOW, IMPERIAL COLLEGE LONDON, KING'S COLLEGE LONDON, LANCASTER, LEEDS, LIVERPOOL, LONDON SCHOOL OF ECONOMICS, LOUGHBOROUGH, MANCHESTER, NEWCASTLE, NOTTINGHAM, OXFORD, SHEFFIELD, SOUTHAMPTON, UNIVERSITY COLLEGE LONDON, WARWICK, YORK
Please check with your university careers service for full details of local events.

MINIMUM ENTRY REQUIREMENTS
2.1 Degree

APPLICATION DEADLINE
Year-round recruitment

FURTHER INFORMATION
www.Top100GraduateEmployers.com
Register now for the latest news, events information and graduate recruitment details for Britain's leading employers.

your future
made with
IBM

What will you make with IBM?

ibm.com/jobs/uk

BEHIND THE
EXCELLENCE

Home to some of the most iconic nameplates ever to take to the road, Jaguar Land Rover has a proud and enviable heritage. One that has seen them continually redefine the global benchmark for quality, performance and innovation and set the standards that others want to follow.

With such momentum behind them, the organisation's future is set to be even more exciting. Increasing demand and significant investment in new products, facilities and markets, means finding the next-generation of innovators who will shape Jaguar Land Rover's future has never been more important.

Reflecting the scale of their ambition is Jaguar Land Rover's extensive and expanding graduate offering. Opportunities lie right across the business in everything from Engineering and Manufacturing disciplines to their Commercial and Business areas.

Whichever role graduates make their own, they'll discover a dedication to excellence runs throughout the business. They'll find a requirement for innovative and creative thinking that pushes the boundaries of their potential, and ensures they develop a rigorous and commercially-focused approach to their work. With ongoing support to gain further professional qualifications and accreditation, in-house training and a thorough induction programme, the graduate scheme has been designed to be as inspiring as the pioneering vehicles they'll help produce.

As would be expected from two of the world's most revered brands, an outstanding range of rewards and benefits await those who have the initiative, vision and drive to contribute to the organisation's global success – including a competitive salary, joining bonus, pension scheme and discounted car purchase scheme. All this and more makes Jaguar Land Rover an enviable place to start the journey and put their excellence in motion.

GRADUATE VACANCIES IN 2015
ENGINEERING
FINANCE
HUMAN RESOURCES
IT
LOGISTICS
MARKETING
PROPERTY
PURCHASING
RESEARCH & DEVELOPMENT
SALES

NUMBER OF VACANCIES
270 graduate jobs

LOCATIONS OF VACANCIES

STARTING SALARY FOR 2015
£29,000
Plus a £2,000 joining bonus.

UNIVERSITY VISITS IN 2014-15
ASTON, BATH, BIRMINGHAM, BRISTOL, BRUNEL, CAMBRIDGE, CARDIFF, DURHAM, EDINBURGH, EXETER, GLASGOW, IMPERIAL COLLEGE LONDON, LANCASTER, LEEDS, LIVERPOOL, LOUGHBOROUGH, MANCHESTER, NEWCASTLE, NOTTINGHAM, OXFORD, READING, SHEFFIELD, SOUTHAMPTON, STRATHCLYDE, TRINITY COLLEGE DUBLIN, WARWICK, YORK
Please check with your university careers service for full details of local events.

MINIMUM ENTRY REQUIREMENTS
2.2 Degree

APPLICATION DEADLINE
31st December 2014

FURTHER INFORMATION
www.Top100GraduateEmployers.com
Register now for the latest news, events information and graduate recruitment details for Britain's leading employers.

EXCELLENCE IN MOTION
CAREERS

BEHIND THE NEXT GENERATION

GRADUATE & UNDERGRADUATE OPPORTUNITIES
ENGINEERING & COMMERCIAL BUSINESS AREAS

Our heritage is enviable. Our future will be breathtaking. As home to two of the world's most iconic brands, there has never been a more exciting time to join our journey. The scale of our ambition is reflected by the ever-expanding breadth of our graduate programmes and undergraduate placements. From our **Manufacturing** and **Engineering** disciplines to our **Commercial** and **Business** functions, this is a place where you'll use your creativity to redefine the benchmark for excellence. Where you'll continually push the boundaries of your own potential. Where you'll develop specialist and commercial skills working alongside an industry-revered team.

Find out more at **jaguarlandrovercareers.com**

John Lewis Partnership

The John Lewis Partnership is a multi-award winning retail business and incorporates two of the high street's most renowned brands – John Lewis and Waitrose. Combining the best of traditional and modern, it has responded to customers' needs to become a truly omni-channel business.

This commitment to innovation and outstanding customer service is part of what makes the John Lewis Partnership so different and successful. But perhaps the most unique aspect is that everyone that joins the organisation becomes a Partner. This means they own a share in the business and get to have a say in how it's run.

And key to its ongoing success are graduates. The organisation is keen to give graduates early responsibility as well as challenges that give them every opportunity to make a difference. The Partnership runs a number of schemes that are all geared up to create future leaders of the business. These fast-paced and stimulating programmes offer real experiences, superb training and support, the chance to work with different individuals and to create a strong graduate community. Exposure to the most successful leaders in retail today, support from a buddy or mentor and a comprehensive induction are also core aspects of development.

A lot is expected in return. A sense of pride in ownership and the ability to make things happen. To deliver excellent service, work together, bring commitment to personal and professional development and openness and adaptability to change are all things that the John Lewis Partnership look for (along with specific generalist or specialist skills of course). Graduates that bring these qualities can expect to start a unique journey with the organisation consistently voted as the nation's most loved retailer.

GRADUATE VACANCIES IN 2015
FINANCE
GENERAL MANAGEMENT
IT
PURCHASING
RETAILING

NUMBER OF VACANCIES
79 graduate jobs

LOCATIONS OF VACANCIES

STARTING SALARY FOR 2015
Dependent on scheme
Please see website for full details.

UNIVERSITY VISITS IN 2014-15
Please check with your university careers service for full details of local events.

MINIMUM ENTRY REQUIREMENTS
Dependent on scheme
Please see website for full details.

APPLICATION DEADLINE
3rd December 2014

FURTHER INFORMATION
www.Top100GraduateEmployers.com
Register now for the latest news, events information and graduate recruitment details for Britain's leading employers.

J.P.Morgan

jpmorgan.com/careers

J.P. Morgan plays a leading role in helping markets grow and companies develop in more than 100 countries, and holds global leadership positions in all its businesses. Their team of employees work tirelessly to do the right thing for their clients, shareholders and the firm every day.

J.P. Morgan makes the most of every individual's talents, not just their technical skills. Each individual is given the tools, training and support needed to help them keep doing first-class business in a first-class way, as the firm has for over 200 years.

Career opportunities are available firm-wide, so it pays to find out as much as possible about the industry, the business areas, the roles on offer and what J.P. Morgan look for before applying. There are pre-internship programmes across many of the lines of business and initiatives such as Spring Week and Winning Women give students a chance to get noticed early – and many interns are hired directly from these programmes.

Internship and graduate opportunities are available in the following areas: CIB Risk, Finance, Human Resources, Investment Banking, Investment Management, Investor Services, Operations, Private Bank, Quantitative Research, Sales, Trading & Research, Technology and Treasury Services.

J.P. Morgan is looking for team players and future leaders with exceptional drive, creativity and interpersonal skills. Impeccable academic credentials are important, but so are achievements outside the classroom.

Working with a team committed to doing their best – and being the best. Earning the trust of their clients. Demanding excellence of employees. That's what it means to be part of J.P. Morgan. Join and help shape the future of one of the most respected financial institutions in the world.

GRADUATE VACANCIES IN 2015
ACCOUNTANCY
FINANCE
HUMAN RESOURCES
INVESTMENT BANKING
IT
RESEARCH & DEVELOPMENT
SALES

NUMBER OF VACANCIES
No fixed quota

LOCATIONS OF VACANCIES

Vacancies also available in Europe, the USA and Asia.

STARTING SALARY FOR 2015
£Competitive

UNIVERSITY VISITS IN 2014-15
BATH, BIRMINGHAM, BRISTOL, CAMBRIDGE, DURHAM, EDINBURGH, EXETER, GLASGOW, HERIOT-WATT, IMPERIAL COLLEGE LONDON, KING'S COLLEGE LONDON, LONDON SCHOOL OF ECONOMICS, LOUGHBOROUGH, MANCHESTER, NOTTINGHAM, OXFORD, SOUTHAMPTON, ST ANDREWS, STRATHCLYDE, UNIVERSITY COLLEGE LONDON, WARWICK
Please check with your university careers service for full details of local events.

MINIMUM ENTRY REQUIREMENTS
2.1 Degree

APPLICATION DEADLINE
30th November 2014

FURTHER INFORMATION
www.Top100GraduateEmployers.com
Register now for the latest news, events information and graduate recruitment details for Britain's leading employers.

WHAT'S SO INTERESTING
ABOUT THIS CREDIT RISK ANALYST?

RICHARD
Analyst, CIB Risk
Photographer/
Fitness Enthusiast

HE STUDIED RUSSIAN AT UNIVERSITY.

Not everyone who works here had the intention of pursuing a career in finance. But they did start out with a passion for excellence, as well as a desire to be challenged to reach their fullest potential. And we've discovered that sometimes our most talented employees come from the unlikeliest of backgrounds.

So we look for people who have the intellectual firepower to help us innovate for our clients. The vision to take the long-term view of their needs. And the boldness to execute their strategies.

To learn more about finance career opportunities, visit our website and apply today.

We want what you're made of.

jpmorgan.com/careers

J.P.Morgan

KPMG

cutting through complexity

KPMG is a global network of professional firms providing Audit, Tax and Advisory services to some of the world's biggest businesses. In the UK alone, KPMG has 22 offices and over 11,000 partners and staff. For graduates, it has a diverse range of programmes offering various professional qualifications.

KPMG believes that all business, all solutions, boil down to one thing: people. That's why whatever KPMG do, they see people first. Championing the human element is a big part of their culture, and to them, their own people are at the heart of their continued success.

But there's no one type of person that succeeds at KPMG. It's a massively diverse business, welcoming all kinds of personalities and characters, skills sets and, indeed, degree disciplines. For any graduate who thrives on responsibility, intellectual challenge, and variety, it really is a great place to start a career.

KPMG also believes in delivering the best. After all, when some of the world's biggest companies hand over their audit, tax or advisory challenges to KPMG, they need to know there's no margin for error. Their clients operate in a huge range of business sectors, and to give them the best service means providing them with experts who really understand them.

The work is definitely challenging. That's why KPMG's graduate programmes offer exceptional training for professional qualifications (with unique, fast-track options and an enviable pass rate few can match), tons of exposure and 'real world, real time' responsibility. It's a great place for graduates to learn and develop their skills – a fast-moving, technology-driven working environment. And they'll be joining a community they'll feel a part of for the rest of their lives.

GRADUATE VACANCIES IN 2015

ACCOUNTANCY
CONSULTING
FINANCE
HUMAN RESOURCES
IT

NUMBER OF VACANCIES
1,000 graduate jobs

LOCATIONS OF VACANCIES

STARTING SALARY FOR 2015
£Competitive
Plus benefits.

UNIVERSITY VISITS IN 2014-15
ABERDEEN, ASTON, BATH, BIRMINGHAM, BRISTOL, CAMBRIDGE, CARDIFF, CITY, DURHAM, EDINBURGH, EXETER, GLASGOW, HERIOT-WATT, IMPERIAL COLLEGE LONDON, KING'S COLLEGE LONDON, LANCASTER, LEEDS, LEICESTER, LIVERPOOL, LONDON SCHOOL OF ECONOMICS, LOUGHBOROUGH, MANCHESTER, NEWCASTLE, NOTTINGHAM, OXFORD, SHEFFIELD, SOUTHAMPTON, ST ANDREWS, STRATHCLYDE, UNIVERSITY COLLEGE LONDON, WARWICK, YORK
Please check with your university careers service for full details of local events.

MINIMUM ENTRY REQUIREMENTS
2.1 Degree
300 UCAS points
Plus minimum B grade in GCSE Maths and English Language (or equivalent). Please see website for specific programme requirements.

APPLICATION DEADLINE
Year-round recruitment
Early application advised.

FURTHER INFORMATION
www.Top100GraduateEmployers.com
Register now for the latest news, events information and graduate recruitment details for Britain's leading employers.

KPMG

cutting through complexity

My **KPMG**

"As you can see, it's made up of a lot of people. Some I see every day. Some maybe less so. But each and every connection I've made here has taught me something. And I know many of them will last for life.

I'd recommend KPMG to any graduate because, no matter which path you take, you'll be working with some of the brightest brains in business with access to the best professional development around."

Katharine, Graduate Trainee

Visit **www.kpmgcareers.co.uk/times100** to find out about careers for graduates from all degree disciplines in **Audit, Tax, Advisory, Technology, Marketing** and **HR.**

SEE **BEHIND THE SCENES** AT **MYKPMG.CO.UK**

L'ORÉAL

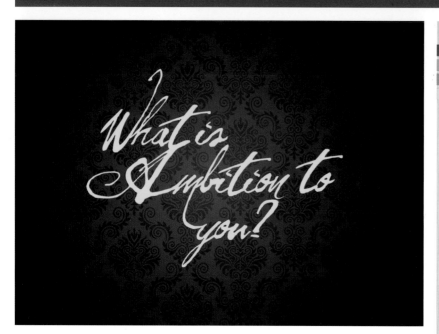

L'Oréal is the number one cosmetics group in the world. Every second, 130 of their products are sold worldwide. Their industry is relentlessly competitive, the business is equally dynamic, and the opportunities they offer are truly outstanding.

Joining L'Oréal means working on some of the most innovative and recognised brands there are. Their 30 global brands reach a billion customers, and their ambition is to reach a billion more. Their portfolio includes world-famous names like L'Oréal Paris, Lancôme, The Body Shop and Diesel – brands that are loved by customers and trusted by professionals worldwide. And their graduates play an important role in their success.

L'Oréal's year-long Management Training Scheme covers four vital areas of the business – Commercial, Marketing, Finance and Supply Chain. Whichever part graduates join, they'll work closely with some of the best people in the industry to tackle high profile projects. For the first time L'Oréal are integrating their programme with The Body Shop International, offering opportunities to work with this iconic retail beauty brand.

Most of the training happens on the job, although it is complemented by a schedule of formal courses. Mentors, buddies and supportive colleagues round off the development experience, which is tailored to each individual graduate.

Along with the training, the experience and a competitive salary, there is one other key benefit – a fantastic working environment. L'Oréal's people are lively, enthusiastic and friendly, and they provide plenty of opportunities for networking and having fun.

For entrepreneurial and ambitious graduates who don't shy away from the big projects, there really is nowhere better to build a career.

GRADUATE VACANCIES IN 2015
FINANCE
LOGISTICS
MARKETING
SALES

NUMBER OF VACANCIES
40 graduate jobs

LOCATIONS OF VACANCIES

STARTING SALARY FOR 2015
£29,000

UNIVERSITY VISITS IN 2014-15
BATH, BIRMINGHAM, CAMBRIDGE, CARDIFF, DURHAM, EDINBURGH, EXETER, LANCASTER, LEEDS, LONDON SCHOOL OF ECONOMICS, LOUGHBOROUGH, MANCHESTER, NEWCASTLE, NORTHUMBRIA, NOTTINGHAM, NOTTINGHAM TRENT, OXFORD, READING, ST ANDREWS, SUSSEX, WARWICK, YORK
Please check with your university careers service for full details of local events.

MINIMUM ENTRY REQUIREMENTS
2.1 Degree
300 UCAS points

APPLICATION DEADLINE
31st December 2014

FURTHER INFORMATION
www.Top100GraduateEmployers.com
Register now for the latest news, events information and graduate recruitment details for Britain's leading employers.

Management Training Scheme / Internship opportunities

Commercial • Marketing • Supply Chain • Finance

Ambition is creating something that two million people "Like"

Ambition means something different to every one of our graduates. For Chetan, it means creating a social media approach that gets adopted by our offices all around the world. For others, it's managing twenty clients in their first two weeks, or showcasing the revenue they have driven. For us, it's about pushing the boundaries and working together to stay number one in our fiercely competitive global market.

What is ambition to you?

Quality products. Quality people.

www.lidlgraduatecareers.co.uk

linkedin.com/company/lidl-uk-gmbh **in**

As one of the UK's retail success stories, Lidl's simple retail philosophy and efficient working practices allow them to focus on what they do best – providing top quality products at the lowest possible prices. Their principles ensure clear structures, simple processes, flat hierarchies and short decision paths.

Lidl is an established international food retailer with more than 10,000 stores trading across Europe. With over 600 stores in the UK alone, they have an impressive schedule of new store openings planned for the next few years and are increasing their portfolio with further warehouses to support their new in-store bakeries.

Uncompromising on quality, they look for the same in their graduates. They are looking for talented, motivated and ambitious people who are excellent communicators and possess good commercial awareness. They offer graduate opportunities in positions across the UK, based in their stores, Regional Distribution Centres and Head Office. A structured and hands-on approach to training allows Lidl graduates to take on early responsibility with support being provided throughout the training by experienced colleagues.

At Lidl, initiative is encouraged with achievements being recognised; this is supported by their promise that internal candidates come first in all career opportunities. In fact, nearly all of their senior professionals started their careers in store operations and have successfully progressed in career paths through sales, property, construction, logistics and a wide range of head office positions.

With opportunities to travel internationally and an excellent rewards package, this could be one of the most exciting opportunities on the market. For graduates who have what it takes to be part of one of the fastest paced industries on the graduate market then Lidl could offer the perfect career opportunity.

GRADUATE VACANCIES IN 2015

GENERAL MANAGEMENT
PROPERTY
PURCHASING
RETAILING
SALES

NUMBER OF VACANCIES
100 graduate jobs

LOCATIONS OF VACANCIES

STARTING SALARY FOR 2015
£38,000

UNIVERSITY VISITS IN 2014-15
ASTON, BIRMINGHAM, DURHAM, EDINBURGH, EXETER, LEEDS, MANCHESTER, NEWCASTLE, NOTTINGHAM, NOTTINGHAM TRENT, READING, ST ANDREWS, STRATHCLYDE, WARWICK
Please check with your university careers service for full details of local events.

MINIMUM ENTRY REQUIREMENTS
2.1 Degree

APPLICATION DEADLINE
Varies by function

FURTHER INFORMATION
www.Top100GraduateEmployers.com
Register now for the latest news, events information and graduate recruitment details for Britain's leading employers.

Quality products. Quality people.

Step into
the limelight.

Are you ready to take the limelight? If you're a natural leader, with the ability to inspire excellence in a team, take the next step towards the best decision you've ever made.

For more information or to download our graduate brochure, please visit:

www.lidlgraduatecareers.co.uk

www.**linklaters**.com/ukgrads
graduate.recruitment@linklaters.com
twitter.com/LinklatersGrads
facebook.com/linklatersgrads
youtube.com/LinklatersUKGrads
linkedin.com/in/linklatersgrads

Linklaters

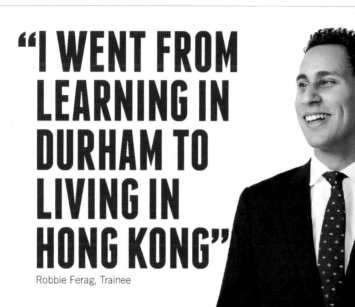

"I WENT FROM LEARNING IN DURHAM TO LIVING IN HONG KONG"

Robbie Ferag, Trainee

As one of the world's most prestigious law firms, Linklaters is the place where graduates can make the most of their talents. Amongst a team of exceptional lawyers, a network of international offices and through unparalleled training and development opportunities, people can truly live their ambitions.

Linklaters attracts and recruits people from a range of subject disciplines and backgrounds. What they all have in common is a desire to achieve their full potential through a career in commercial law.

Linklaters helps its trainees achieve their ambitions by providing an outstanding environment in which to succeed. For non-law graduates, it starts with the Graduate Diploma in Law, giving them all the legal knowledge required to start their professional training. All graduates then come together to complete the bespoke Legal Practice Course.

Once the initial training is complete, it's time to begin working on real client matters through four six-month seats in Linklaters' global practice groups. Each seat not only builds skills and expertise in a particular area, but with ongoing training, feedback and support, it develops the professional and commercial skills that every successful lawyer needs.

As Linklaters believes in continuous learning, the unique Linklaters Law and Business School delivers the tools, knowledge and confidence for lawyers throughout their careers.

What's more, with complex and high-profile deals across their global network of 29 offices and beyond, international secondment opportunities and great rewards, Linklaters offers its trainees broad and rich experiences to springboard their careers.

GRADUATE VACANCIES IN 2015
LAW

NUMBER OF VACANCIES
110 graduate jobs
For training contracts starting in 2017.

LOCATIONS OF VACANCIES

STARTING SALARY FOR 2015
£40,000
Plus insurance, a concierge service, in-house medical and gym, and eligibility for bonus.

UNIVERSITY VISITS IN 2014-15
BELFAST, BIRMINGHAM, BRISTOL, CAMBRIDGE, CARDIFF, DURHAM, EDINBURGH, EXETER, GLASGOW, KING'S COLLEGE LONDON, LANCASTER, LEEDS, LONDON SCHOOL OF ECONOMICS, MANCHESTER, NEWCASTLE, NOTTINGHAM, OXFORD, QUEEN MARY LONDON, SCHOOL OF AFRICAN STUDIES, SHEFFIELD, SOUTHAMPTON, ST ANDREWS, TRINITY COLLEGE DUBLIN, UNIVERSITY COLLEGE DUBLIN, UNIVERSITY COLLEGE LONDON, WARWICK, YORK
Please check with your university careers service for full details of local events.

MINIMUM ENTRY REQUIREMENTS
2.1 Degree

APPLICATION DEADLINE
Varies by function
Please see website for full details.

FURTHER INFORMATION
www.Top100GraduateEmployers.com
Register now for the latest news, events information and graduate recruitment details for Britain's leading employers.

Linklaters

What do you want from your career in commercial law? To work on the most exciting and high-profile deals in a world-leading law firm? To receive top-class training from the brightest talent in the legal sector? To be generously rewarded throughout your career, including through global opportunities? Whatever your goal, we are committed to maximising the potential of our people.

Join Linklaters to live your ambition.

www.linklaters.com/ukgrads

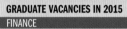
LLOYD'S

Lloyd's is the world's specialist insurance market, insuring some of the world's most complex risks, from hurricanes to terrorism, sporting events to space travel, cybercrime to fine art. Based in the City of London, in the iconic Lloyd's building, it has increasing business and presence in more than 200 countries and territories around the world.

As well as working in the centre of the City, at the heart of the insurance industry, graduates at Lloyd's are provided with a holistic view of the market covering claims, underwriting, broking and the Corporation on the generalist programme. Lloyd's also offers an inspiring eight week summer internship for undergraduates looking for insight before choosing their career path.

Graduates explore the many roles that Lloyd's has to offer by rotation, experiencing anything from managing relationships with international regulators, to examining the potential impact of a catastrophe, to helping develop insight into emerging risks. There is a chance to shape the future as Lloyd's needs sharp, commercial thinkers to develop new approaches and products to meet the needs of an ever changing global outlook.

Placements offer a six month opportunity to undertake a live project with real responsibility. Lloyd's makes sure everyone is confident and up to speed with everything before they start with a thorough induction and continuous training and support.

Lloyd's is looking for graduates from any discipline with sharp analytic and problem solving skills, numerical ability, openness to change and strong relationship building capability. With their impressive benefits package, intellectual challenge and real career building opportunities in the heart of the City, Lloyd's is a superb choice.

GRADUATE VACANCIES IN 2015
FINANCE

NUMBER OF VACANCIES
12-15 graduate jobs

LOCATIONS OF VACANCIES

STARTING SALARY FOR 2015
£26,000
Plus £1,000 every six months for 18 months.

UNIVERSITY VISITS IN 2014-15
KENT, LEICESTER, LONDON SCHOOL OF ECONOMICS, NOTTINGHAM, WARWICK
Please check with your university careers service for full details of local events.

MINIMUM ENTRY REQUIREMENTS
2.2 Degree

APPLICATION DEADLINE
6th January 2015

FURTHER INFORMATION
www.Top100GraduateEmployers.com
Register now for the latest news, events information and graduate recruitment details for Britain's leading employers.

A NEW GENERATION OF RISKS NEEDS THE NEXT GENERATION OF THINKERS.

DRONES_

NASA's exploratory research into using drones to monitor volcanic activity is part of the new generation of risk for which Lloyd's is at the forefront.

Shape the future with the Lloyd's graduate programme_

WWW.LLOYDS.COM/FUTURETHINKERS

@LloydsofLondon   www.facebook.com/lloyds

Lloyds Banking Group is one of the UK's leading financial institutions. With brands including Lloyds, Halifax and Bank of Scotland, one third of the population has a relationship with the Group. With such a diverse portfolio of brands, it has the range of far-reaching career opportunities to match.

Underpinning its entire business is a pledge to help Britain prosper and a vision to become the UK's best bank for customers. The Group is committed to creating innovative, better-value products and services, and strong and sustainable returns.

The Group is a place where talented individuals can explore their potential and find a more meaningful career path. As well as easy access to experienced senior professionals, graduates are given true autonomy to take their development to new levels. With real responsibility from day one, there is plenty of opportunity to shape the future of the organisation and the way people will bank in the future. The emphasis is always on project ownership, collaboration, ethics, innovation and the strongest customer advocate mindset. Robust mentoring and support systems are in place, as well as formal training, and opportunities to study for recognised professional qualifications. The individuals who thrive in this environment are those who create a positive impact through their own work, and that of others.

This year, the Graduate Programme includes roles such as Customer Relationship and Service (including Retail, Insurance, Commercial, Corporate Banking and Financial Markets); Innovation, IT and Digital; Professional Careers (Finance, Audit, Risk and HR); and Strategy/Service Excellence such as Group Operations. Each programme offers a unique experience and caters for different personalities and career aspirations – and every moment is an exciting opportunity.

GRADUATE VACANCIES IN 2015

CONSULTING
FINANCE
GENERAL MANAGEMENT
HUMAN RESOURCES
INVESTMENT BANKING
IT
MARKETING

NUMBER OF VACANCIES
Around 400 graduate jobs

LOCATIONS OF VACANCIES

STARTING SALARY FOR 2015
£28,000-£38,000
Plus a £3,000 sign-on incentive (an extra allowance for London placements), a laptop & mobile phone

UNIVERSITY VISITS IN 2014-15
ASTON, BATH, BIRMINGHAM, BRISTOL, CAMBRIDGE, EXETER, LANCASTER, LEEDS, OXFORD, QUEEN MARY LONDON, WARWICK
Please check with your university careers service for full details of local events.

MINIMUM ENTRY REQUIREMENTS
2.1 Degree
300 UCAS points
Relevant degree required for some roles.

APPLICATION DEADLINE
31st December 2014

FURTHER INFORMATION
www.Top100GraduateEmployers.com
Register now for the latest news, events information and graduate recruitment details for Britain's leading employers.

LLOYDS
BANKING
GROUP

DISCOVER WHAT MATTERS

For those who want a role that matters in life. A role in business.
In communities. In society. For those who want to pursue a career
with far-reaching significance. For those who don't just want a job,
lloydsbankinggrouptalent.com

Say yes to M&S

Amazing things can happen when a graduate says "yes" to M&S. Amazing, exciting, incredible things, and that's just for starters. After all, M&S is a company with big plans – plans involving cutting-edge technology, catwalk fashion, delicious food, and growing the talents of the sharpest graduates around.

Saying "yes" to hearing what M&S can offer is where it all begins. From Retail Management through to IT, Logistics, Marketing and beyond, each M&S graduate programme comes packed with unique opportunities for bright people to achieve the best for themselves and the business.

Career progression is as impressive as the programmes are varied. For example, starting in Retail Management could lead to Commercial Manager level in as little as 12 months. Whichever part of the business a graduate joins, the end of the programme signals the start of a rewarding career with M&S – one where they'll be in an excellent position to achieve their potential as they help one of Britain's best-loved brands do the same.

The fact is, this is something of a golden age for graduates at M&S. With retail moving faster than ever before, those who join the company now will be building the M&S of the future. Whether it's spotting today's trends and turning them into tomorrow's reality, refining retail channels and enhancing shopping experiences, or developing products and services on offer, it's all for the taking at M&S.

For those with high standards, a hard work ethic and an unwavering commitment to doing the right thing, the future's waiting at M&S – along with a competitive salary and a host of other great benefits. Now all that's left to do is say "yes".

GRADUATE VACANCIES IN 2015

GENERAL MANAGEMENT
HUMAN RESOURCES
IT
LOGISTICS
MARKETING
PURCHASING
RESEARCH & DEVELOPMENT
RETAILING

NUMBER OF VACANCIES
200 graduate jobs

LOCATIONS OF VACANCIES

STARTING SALARY FOR 2015
£23,500-£28,000

UNIVERSITY VISITS IN 2014-15
ASTON, BRISTOL, CAMBRIDGE, CARDIFF, EDINBURGH, LEEDS, LOUGHBOROUGH, SHEFFIELD, SURREY
Please check with your university careers service for full details of local events.

MINIMUM ENTRY REQUIREMENTS
2.1 Degree
Relevant degree required for some roles.

APPLICATION DEADLINE
Mid December 2014

FURTHER INFORMATION
www.Top100GraduateEmployers.com
Register now for the latest news, events information and graduate recruitment details for Britain's leading employers.

I said
yes

"Now 63.2 million people like my work
– and one person loves it." Sam Davey

Say yes to M&S and you may well find yourself falling in love with what
you do. You'll be working for one of the UK's most cherished brands,
helping us build an exciting future. All while enjoying the training,
development and support you need to really achieve your ambitions.

Say yes to discovering more about our graduate programmes and
business placements by visiting www.marksandspencergrads.com

Applications open 1 September and close mid December 2014

MARS

Start your own story.

Think 'work, rest and play'. Think M&M's, Uncle Ben's, Pedigree, Whiskas and Wrigley, iconic billion-dollar brands. Think the world's third-largest food company with international operations in 370 locations. Know what makes Mars special? Think again.

Sure, Mars is one of the world's leading food companies, but it's more like a community than a corporate. Because it's still privately owned. And that means it's a place without any of the trappings of typical big business. It has a sense of humanity and a lack of vanity around leadership. It's somewhere that encourages open communication and collaboration, where people can get to grips with challenging work and take on high levels of responsibility early on.

The flat, open structure is a big plus for graduates when it comes to grabbing the opportunity to shape Mars' future. It makes for a truly creative and dynamic environment, whichever programme graduates join on. But it takes more than just freedom and responsibility to create the Mars leaders of the future. What graduates at Mars get is high levels of responsibility, a variety of possibilities and the opportunity to improve things for everyone else along the way.

Mars provides a fantastic support structure, financial sponsorship to pursue professional qualifications, extensive learning and development opportunities and personal mentoring from some of the brightest and best people in the industry. All Mars employees are called associates, and are treated as individuals, not numbers, driving their own performance and development.

In return, Mars gives its associates the autonomy to grab each and every opportunity that presents itself, and commit to improving how Mars treats its customers, communities and the planet. So that ultimately, they can make Mars mean more.

GRADUATE VACANCIES IN 2015

ENGINEERING
FINANCE
GENERAL MANAGEMENT
MARKETING
PURCHASING
RESEARCH & DEVELOPMENT
SALES

NUMBER OF VACANCIES
35 graduate jobs

LOCATIONS OF VACANCIES

Vacancies also available in Europe.

STARTING SALARY FOR 2015
£28,300-£30,000
Plus a £2,000 joining bonus.

UNIVERSITY VISITS IN 2014-15
BATH, BIRMINGHAM, BRISTOL, DURHAM, EXETER, IMPERIAL COLLEGE LONDON, LEEDS, LOUGHBOROUGH, MANCHESTER, NOTTINGHAM, READING, SHEFFIELD, SOUTHAMPTON, UNIVERSITY COLLEGE LONDON, WARWICK
Please check with your university careers service for full details of local events.

MINIMUM ENTRY REQUIREMENTS
2.1 Degree
280-300 UCAS points
Relevant degree required for some roles.

APPLICATION DEADLINE
28th November 2014

FURTHER INFORMATION
www.Top100GraduateEmployers.com
Register now for the latest news, events information and graduate recruitment details for Britain's leading employers.

When the heat was on, Órla had a cool idea.

We love it when demand for our products soars. But in the Middle East and Africa, demand for MALTESERS® was growing so fast that we simply couldn't keep up. Enter Órla, from our Management Development Programme. When we asked her to create a global demand plan she didn't break a sweat. Instead, she considered all the facts and successfully presented her case – for building a brand new production line on the other side of the world. It was a bold idea, but the potential returns were huge. Which left just one problem: how could we meet global demand for MALTESERS® in the meantime? Órla had an idea for that too – introducing a new superfast wrapping machine in the UK. It can wrap more than double the number of bags per minute than before, meaning we can keep our fans happy the world over. It just goes to show. Give people freedom and responsibility, and they'll go further than you ever imagined. **mars.co.uk/graduates**

MAKE IT MEAN MORE | **MARS**

Training and developing people has been at the heart of McDonald's business throughout the 40 years in the UK. Each year, the company invests £43 million in developing its people and providing opportunities to the 95,000 employees to progress, whilst achieving nationally recognised qualifications.

McDonald's arrived in the UK in 1974 and currently operates 1,225 restaurants, employing 95,000 people. The company has a proven track record of career progression; with the entire UK Operations executive team starting their careers on the graduate Trainee Manager programme. Prospective managers can create a long-term career with one of the world's most recognised and successful brands.

A graduate job at McDonald's is focused on restaurant management – it involves overseeing the performance and development of an average 80 employees, and identifying ways in which to improve customer service, build sales and profitability. Following the training period, which can last up to six months, Trainee Managers are promoted to Assistant Managers and become part of the core restaurant management team. Successful Trainee Managers can, in future, progress to managing all aspects of a £multi-million business – opportunities can then arise to progress to area management roles or secondments in support departments. Trainee Managers need to be logical thinkers, have a great attitude and be committed to delivering a great customer experience.

Working for a progressive company has its perks – including a host of benefits such as a quarterly bonus scheme, six weeks holiday, meal allowance, private healthcare and access to discounts at over 1,600 retailers.

GRADUATE VACANCIES IN 2015
GENERAL MANAGEMENT
RETAILING

NUMBER OF VACANCIES
250-350 graduate jobs

LOCATIONS OF VACANCIES

STARTING SALARY FOR 2015
£18,500-£21,500

UNIVERSITY VISITS IN 2014-15
NOTTINGHAM TRENT
Please check with your university careers service for full details of local events.

APPLICATION DEADLINE
Year-round recruitment

FURTHER INFORMATION
www.Top100GraduateEmployers.com
Register now for the latest news, events information and graduate recruitment details for Britain's leading employers.

The McDonald's Trainee Manager Programme is the first step to managing a £multi-million restaurant employing 80 staff.

After six months training and learning all the basics, our Trainee Managers are promoted to Assistant Managers - but if you've got the drive and ambition, there's no limit to how far you can go.

To find out more about working and learning with us visit
mcdonalds.co.uk/people

Sammy Jo
Stockport

TRAINEE MANAGER

McKinsey&Company

McKinsey & Company helps world-leading clients in the public, private and third sectors to meet their biggest strategic, operational and organisational challenges. Their goal is to provide distinctive and long-lasting performance improvements – in short, it is about having an impact. Making a difference.

As a consultant in this truly global firm, graduates will have the opportunity to work with colleagues and clients from all around the world. They will come into contact with CEOs, government leaders and the foremost charitable organisations, and work together with them on their most exciting and challenging issues.

Working as part of a small team, and dedicated to one project at a time, graduates will be fully involved from the very start of their first project. No two weeks will be the same: from gathering and analysing data, to interviewing stakeholders or presenting findings to clients, the range of industries and business issues to which successful applicants have exposure will mean that they are constantly acquiring new skills and experience. Bright, motivated newcomers can expect their ideas and opinions to be encouraged and valued, right from day one.

Graduates will also enjoy world-class personal and professional development. Formal training programmes, coupled with a culture of mentoring and coaching, will provide the best possible support.

Working in consulting is challenging, but McKinsey encourages a healthy work-life balance. Successful applicants will find like-minded individuals, and a thriving range of groups, initiatives and events that bring people together.

McKinsey & Company is welcoming applications for both full time and summer internship applications.

GRADUATE VACANCIES IN 2015

CONSULTING

NUMBER OF VACANCIES
No fixed quota

LOCATIONS OF VACANCIES

Vacancies also available elsewhere in the world.

STARTING SALARY FOR 2015
£Competitive

UNIVERSITY VISITS IN 2014-15
BELFAST, BRISTOL, CAMBRIDGE, EDINBURGH, IMPERIAL COLLEGE LONDON, LONDON SCHOOL OF ECONOMICS, OXFORD, TRINITY COLLEGE DUBLIN, UNIVERSITY COLLEGE DUBLIN, WARWICK
Please check with your university careers service for full details of local events.

MINIMUM ENTRY REQUIREMENTS
2.1 Degree

APPLICATION DEADLINE
30th October 2014

FURTHER INFORMATION
www.Top100GraduateEmployers.com
Register now for the latest news, events information and graduate recruitment details for Britain's leading employers.

Don't just come to work. Come to change.

We welcome applications from all degree disciplines.

Deadline dates:

Full time opportunities 30 October 2014

Internship opportunities 29 January 2015

METROPOLITAN POLICE

TOTAL POLICING

www.metpolicecareers.co.uk

The Metropolitan Police Service (MPS) is respected throughout the world as a leading authority on policing. It is their job to make London a safe place for the millions of people who live there – plus the millions more who work in and visit the capital each year.

Reducing crime, and the fear of crime, in a vibrant multicultural city requires an equally diverse workforce. The MPS must continue to recruit the brightest and the best people from every background. They need the kind of individuals who can forge close relationships, build trust and understand the complex issues that affect different communities. With the full spectrum of skills, knowledge and experience they can make London safer for everybody.

With thousands of people, the MPS is one of the capital's largest employers. Many of these individuals work as frontline police officers with the people of London. Dealing with the day-to-day challenges of policing one of the world's largest cities is one of the most important, rewarding and absorbing roles around. In order for them to fulfil their roles, however, they rely on the support of a host of people working behind the scenes.

From Human Resources, IT to Accountancy, Forensics and Marketing and Communications, the MPS encompasses every department found in a large corporate organisation (and a few that are not). So there is a wide range of roles for graduates to choose from – all of which come with the in-depth training and support necessary to progress their careers.

Working for the Metropolitan Police Service can open doors to many different areas, such as voluntary work as a special constable (volunteer police officer).

But whatever role they play, graduates can be sure of joining an organisation with unique challenges.

GRADUATE VACANCIES IN 2015

POLICING

NUMBER OF VACANCIES
To be confirmed

LOCATIONS OF VACANCIES

STARTING SALARY FOR 2015
Dependent on scheme
New Police Constables will be paid circa £28,000.

UNIVERSITY VISITS IN 2014-15
LONDON
Please check with your university careers service for full details of local events.

APPLICATION DEADLINE
Please see website for full details.

FURTHER INFORMATION
www.Top100GraduateEmployers.com
Register now for the latest news, events information and graduate recruitment details for Britain's leading employers.

SOME CAREERS IMPROVE COMPANIES. YOU'LL TRANSFORM COMMUNITIES.

BE THERE FOR LONDON

CAREERS IN THE METROPOLITAN POLICE SERVICE

You've spent the last few years learning, growing, honing your skills and laying the groundwork for a career that's worthy of your degree. To find out more about the range of career paths and graduate opportunities, visit **www.metpolicecareers.co.uk**

METROPOLITAN POLICE   TOTAL POLICING

NEW SCOTLAND YARD

MI5 helps safeguard the UK against threats to national security including terrorism and espionage. It investigates suspect individuals and organisations to gather intelligence relating to security threats. MI5 also advises the critical national infrastructure on protective security measures, to help them reduce their vulnerability.

Graduates from a range of backgrounds join MI5 for stimulating and rewarding careers. Some join to use languages such as Russian or Mandarin, or graduates with a passion for technology can join our two year Technology Graduate Development Programme. This programme will develop the skills, understanding and competencies required to undertake a range of roles within MI5's pioneering IT function. It is specifically designed to deepen knowledge, hone technical skills, consolidate a portfolio of work experience and start work towards gaining a relevant professional qualification, leading to a rewarding career at the very forefront of technology.

The Intelligence Officer Development Programme is a structured programme that covers the first 3-5 years of an Intelligence Officer's career and is designed to help new joiners learn about investigations before they lead them. Those on the programme are deployed into posts that offer the development of skills with direct relevance to intelligence work. After completing one post of two years or two posts of one year, and subject to successful completion of performance reviews and assessments, those on the programme will then be eligible to undertake Foundation Investigative Training (FIT). After successfully completing FIT, and after an investigative posting, those on the programme will be fully trained Intelligence Officers and can choose to remain in investigative work, or move into an operational or corporate role.

GRADUATE VACANCIES IN 2015

GENERAL MANAGEMENT

IT

NUMBER OF VACANCIES
80+ graduate jobs

LOCATIONS OF VACANCIES

STARTING SALARY FOR 2015
£25,000-£30,000

UNIVERSITY VISITS IN 2014-15
Please check with your university careers service for full details of local events.

MINIMUM ENTRY REQUIREMENTS
Relevant degree required for some roles.

APPLICATION DEADLINE
Varies by function

FURTHER INFORMATION
www.Top100GraduateEmployers.com
Register now for the latest news, events information and graduate recruitment details for Britain's leading employers.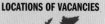

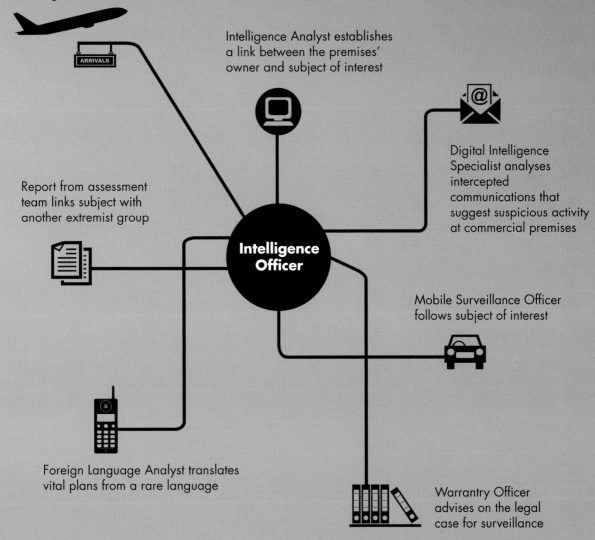

Senior Manager asks for your opinion on the future direction of the investigation

Intelligence Analyst establishes a link between the premises' owner and subject of interest

Digital Intelligence Specialist analyses intercepted communications that suggest suspicious activity at commercial premises

Report from assessment team links subject with another extremist group

Intelligence Officer

Mobile Surveillance Officer follows subject of interest

Foreign Language Analyst translates vital plans from a rare language

Warrantry Officer advises on the legal case for surveillance

Graduate Careers at MI5

MI5 helps safeguard the UK against threats to national security including terrorism and espionage. Graduates from a range of backgrounds and degree disciplines join us for stimulating, rewarding careers. Some join to use languages such as Russian or Mandarin Chinese, others join the Intelligence Officer Development Programme, designed to help you learn about investigations before you lead them. Graduates with a passion for technology can join our Technology Graduate Development Programme. We recruit for these roles several times a year. To find out more, visit our website www.mi5.gov.uk/careers

To apply to MI5 you must be a born or naturalised British citizen, over 18 years old and normally have lived in the UK for nine of the last ten years. You should not discuss your application, other than with your partner or a close family member, providing that they are British. They should also be made aware of the importance of discretion.

When smart, creative, passionate people get together, the result can be astounding and the opportunities limitless. Microsoft are empowering their customers to do more and achieve more. They are obsessing about building products to solve hard challenges. They are reinventing productivity.

As Microsoft continue to accelerate their transformation into a cloud-first and mobile-first world, the opportunity to stretch existing skills and build new ones is there for the taking. Curiosity, questions and ideas are encouraged, valued and respected. Graduates will benefit from being part of an organisation that's re-inventing productivity through technologies that will empower everyone to do more and achieve more.

Graduate opportunities provide individuals with a real job role alongside the perfect training platform to launch their career. With opportunities in Sales, Technical, Consulting or Project Management, graduates will work on major projects from day one. As well as learning from senior colleagues and mentors from across the business, they'll have the chance to meet peers from around the world on a number of international networking and training events.

Highlights of the 18-month training include: a four day induction which provides a spring-board into the business; mentoring and a self-learning curriculum, plus international formal training camps aimed at developing cross-profession skills and specialist expertise.

Microsoft also run an award-winning one year internship scheme. With a comprehensive induction followed by in-depth on-the-job learning and skills training, it's an insightful introduction to Microsoft. Intern roles are hugely varied and stretch across a number of exciting business areas including Online Advertising, Bing, Xbox, Studios and more.

GRADUATE VACANCIES IN 2015

CONSULTING

IT

SALES

NUMBER OF VACANCIES
36 graduate jobs

LOCATIONS OF VACANCIES

STARTING SALARY FOR 2015
£34,700
Plus a sign-on bonus.

UNIVERSITY VISITS IN 2014-15
ASTON, BATH, BIRMINGHAM, CARDIFF, EXETER, IMPERIAL COLLEGE LONDON, LOUGHBOROUGH, MANCHESTER, NOTTINGHAM TRENT, READING, SURREY, UNIVERSITY COLLEGE LONDON, WARWICK
Please check with your university careers service for full details of local events.

MINIMUM ENTRY REQUIREMENTS
2.1 Degree

APPLICATION DEADLINE
Mid November
Early application advised.

FURTHER INFORMATION
www.Top100GraduateEmployers.com
Register now for the latest news, events information and graduate recruitment details for Britain's leading employers.

MAKE IT. BREAK IT. MAKE IT BETTER.

When smart, creative, passionate people get together, the result can be astounding and the opportunities limitless. Microsoft are looking ahead and empowering their customers to do more and achieve more. They are obsessing about building products to solve hard challenges. They are reinventing productivity. As a graduate you will help build the future in a cloud-first, mobile-first world.

www.microsoft.co.uk/students

 Microsoft

GREAT PLACE TO WORK® Best Workplaces 2014 Europe

www.mdlzearlycareers.co.uk
facebook.com/mondelezinternational f
linkedin.com/company/mondelezinternational/careers in   twitter.com/MDLZ y

Mondelēz International

Mondelēz International is the name behind much loved brands like Cadbury, Halls, Milka, Belvita and Toblerone. They market their products in 165 countries, enjoy annual net revenues of $35 billion and employ 110,000 people worldwide. In short, they're a global snacking powerhouse on a mission to create delicious moments of joy.

Created in 2012, Mondelēz International is the world's biggest start-up company. They're ranked first in biscuits, chocolate, confectionery and powdered beverages, and second in gum and coffee. As a result, the variety and scope of opportunities is exceptional – all in a fast-paced, constantly changing environment.

The graduate programme at Mondelēz International is individually tailored, so each person who joins will feel very special indeed. From day one graduates on the programme will experience an exciting journey, with carefully considered placements that offer the chance to make an impact and grow. So rather than being on a designated path, everyone gets to decide where their career will take them.

Mondelēz International looks for graduates with great ideas and the motivation and commercial spirit to apply them. Solid academic results and the ability to adapt to the evolving needs of a global organisation are essential.

In return, they offer continuous development opportunities, lots of exposure to industry experts and a real chance to become a future leader of the business. They also offer excellent support in the form of a buddy and mentor, a generous salary, impressive benefits and all the chocolate a graduate can eat!

Working across different brands, categories and 13 different locations in the UK and Ireland, no two days will be the same. Graduates will even have the chance to cast the net wider to the rest of Europe, or perhaps even the world.

GRADUATE VACANCIES IN 2015

ENGINEERING
FINANCE
HUMAN RESOURCES
LOGISTICS
MARKETING
RESEARCH & DEVELOPMENT
SALES

NUMBER OF VACANCIES
Around 40 graduate jobs

LOCATIONS OF VACANCIES

Vacancies also available in Europe.

STARTING SALARY FOR 2015
£27,000-£29,500
Plus a joining bonus and an annual performance bonus.

UNIVERSITY VISITS IN 2014-15
ASTON, BATH, BIRMINGHAM, BRISTOL, CARDIFF, DURHAM, EXETER, LANCASTER, LEEDS, LOUGHBOROUGH, MANCHESTER, NEWCASTLE, NOTTINGHAM, OXFORD, READING, UNIVERSITY COLLEGE LONDON, WARWICK
Please check with your university careers service for full details of local events.

MINIMUM ENTRY REQUIREMENTS
2.1 Degree

APPLICATION DEADLINE
15th November 2014

FURTHER INFORMATION
www.Top100GraduateEmployers.com
Register now for the latest news, events information and graduate recruitment details for Britain's leading employers.

Mondelēz International

big enough to make the world's most delicious brands.

small enough to look after the people behind them.

the power of big. and small.

We're Mondelēz International. You may not have heard of us, but you've almost certainly heard of our brands. Brands like Cadbury, Oreo, Trebor, Toblerone and Philadelphia. Names known and loved all around the world. Even though we're a global snacking powerhouse, we never forget what got us to where we are today – the people behind our products. That's why we do everything we can to create an inspiring place to work, and why we'll offer you real exposure to industry experts and continuous development opportunities.

To learn more about who we are and the opportunities available for apprentices, A-level school-leavers, interns, graduates and field sales execs, visit mdlzearlycareers.co.uk

creme egg

Morgan Stanley

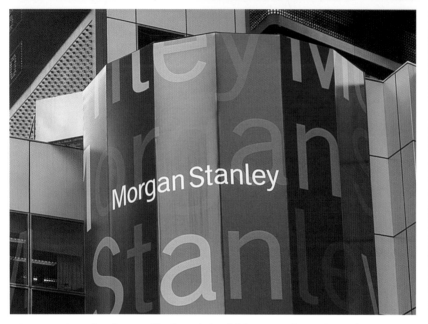

GRADUATE VACANCIES IN 2015

FINANCE

HUMAN RESOURCES

INVESTMENT BANKING

IT

NUMBER OF VACANCIES
No fixed quota

LOCATIONS OF VACANCIES

Vacancies also available in Europe.

STARTING SALARY FOR 2015
£Competitive
Plus benefits and a discretionary bonus.

UNIVERSITY VISITS IN 2014-15
BATH, BELFAST, BRISTOL, CAMBRIDGE, CITY,
DURHAM, EDINBURGH, EXETER, GLASGOW,
HERIOT-WATT, IMPERIAL COLLEGE LONDON,
KING'S COLLEGE LONDON, LONDON
SCHOOL OF ECONOMICS, LOUGHBOROUGH,
NOTTINGHAM, OXFORD, ST ANDREWS,
STIRLING, STRATHCLYDE, ULSTER,
UNIVERSITY COLLEGE DUBLIN, UNIVERSITY
COLLEGE LONDON, WARWICK, YORK
*Please check with your university careers
service for full details of local events.*

MINIMUM ENTRY REQUIREMENTS
2.1 Degree

APPLICATION DEADLINE
Varies by function
Early application advised.

FURTHER INFORMATION
www.Top100GraduateEmployers.com
*Register now for the latest news, events
information and graduate recruitment
details for Britain's leading employers.*

Morgan Stanley has a distinguished history of serving clients for over 75 years. Since its founding in 1935, the firm has been known for the important clients it serves, its innovative approach to solving complex problems, and its agility in embracing change.

Morgan Stanley is a firm that inspires people to be their best – and always finds new opportunities to offer them. Its mission is to build a community of talent that can deliver the finest financial thinking and products in the world.

There is no typical person at Morgan Stanley. People come from a wide variety of backgrounds and interests – all are high achievers who share integrity, intellectual curiosity and the desire to work in a collegial environment. Individuality is prized and people are encouraged to be themselves.

Morgan Stanley offers a variety of Graduate Programmes and internship opportunities for students who demonstrate the entrepreneurial drive, team working and communication skills to take the business forward. All Graduate Programmes are designed to provide graduates with the knowledge and toolkit they require to quickly become effective and successful professionals in their chosen area. Training is not limited to the first weeks or months on the job but continues throughout the graduate's career.

The summer and industrial placement programmes are considered first class and designed to attract, develop and continually assess those students who are most likely to succeed in the long-term. Through classroom-based and on-the-job training, seminars, regular mentoring, social events and the experience of working with top people in the industry throughout a period of either 10 or 48 weeks, students gain a unique insight into the industry and Morgan Stanley's culture – all necessary foundations for a truly exceptional and rewarding career.

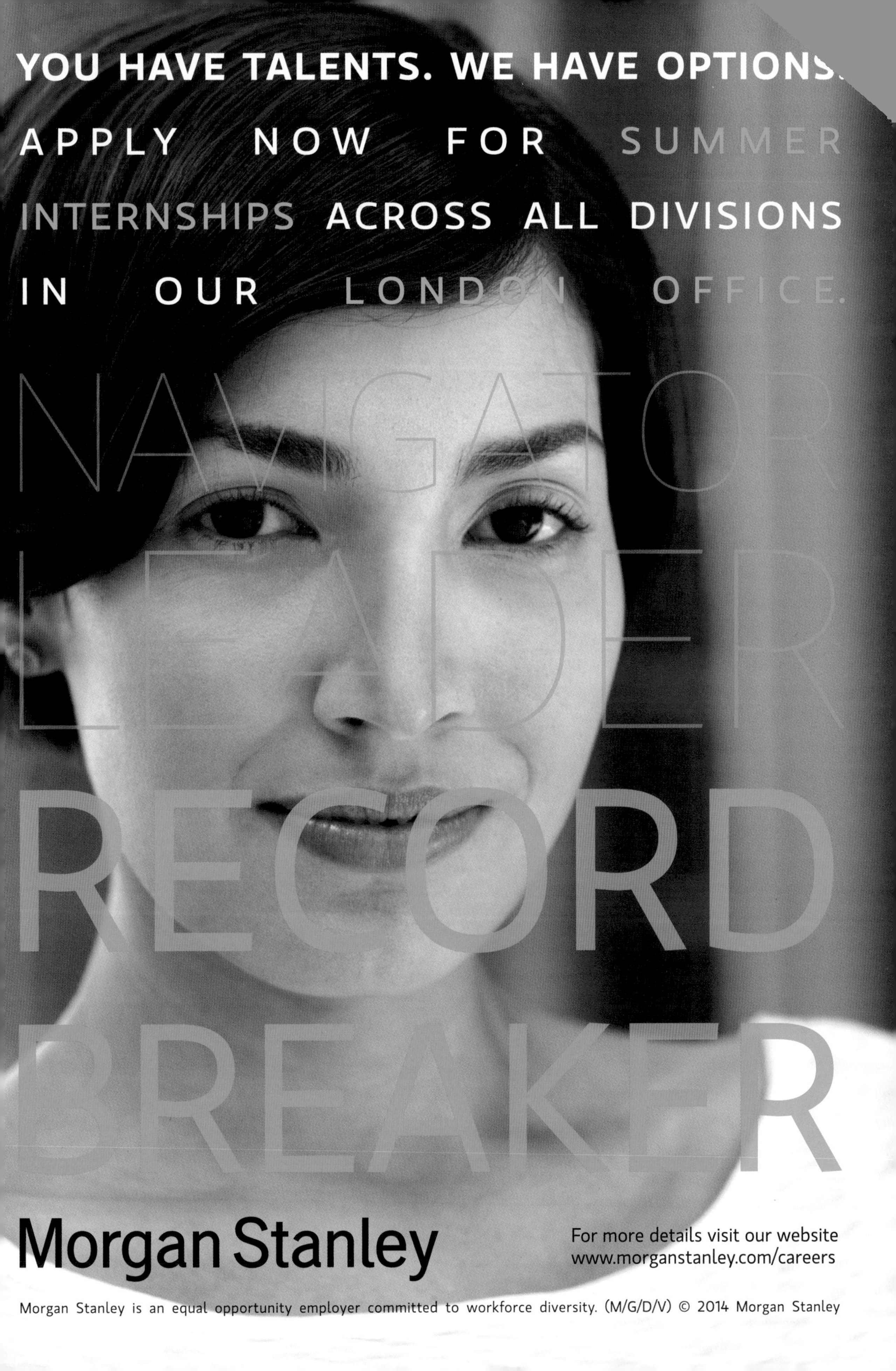

YOU HAVE TALENTS. WE HAVE OPTIONS.
APPLY NOW FOR SUMMER INTERNSHIPS ACROSS ALL DIVISIONS IN OUR LONDON OFFICE.
NAVIGATOR
LEADER
RECORD BREAKER
Morgan Stanley
For more details visit our website
www.morganstanley.com/careers
Morgan Stanley is an equal opportunity employer committed to workforce diversity. (M/G/D/V) © 2014 Morgan Stanley

Join our
AWARD WINNING GRADUATE SCHEMES

GRADUATE RECRUITMENT AWARDS ★WINNER★

MORRISONS

Morrisons is much, much more than a big food retailer. They are a business in transformation, with a passion for new ideas and are well on their way to becoming their customers' favourite food shop. Proud to be different, Morrisons grow their own – both their talent and their food.

Unlike the other big food retailers, Morrisons not only buy from carefully selected suppliers, but also own their own production and supply chain, making them the UK's second largest food producer. This gives them full control of the quality, availability and cost of their food and means they can operate to the shortest lead times in the business.

With such a broad range of schemes available in the one company, graduates can learn fast and go far. Whether joining one of their many Head Office based schemes or in Manufacturing, Logistics or Retail – this range of opportunities simply isn't available anywhere else. Moving in many directions across the organisation, Morrisons graduates have the best chance of reaching the top.

Playing to strengths is how Morrisons grow their own key players and leaders. Having won numerous top employer awards, they are keen supporters of developing graduates' careers. As tomorrow's managers move around, they get lots of new responsibilities – encouraged and backed up all the way by senior managers, personal mentors and 'buddies'.

Doing things smarter, more simply and with passion is refocussing the business. They are rolling their online shopping site nationwide as well as more M local convenience stores and are making the produce and craft skills of Morrisons 'Market Street' the stars of the show.

Morrisons is a great place to work where people are well led, involved and inspired. Talent is an investment and being different is valued.

GRADUATE VACANCIES IN 2015

FINANCE
GENERAL MANAGEMENT
HUMAN RESOURCES
IT
LOGISTICS
MARKETING
PROPERTY
RETAILING

NUMBER OF VACANCIES
100+ graduate jobs

LOCATIONS OF VACANCIES

STARTING SALARY FOR 2015
£25,000

UNIVERSITY VISITS IN 2014-15
BRADFORD, EDINBURGH, HULL, KEELE, LANCASTER, LEEDS, LIVERPOOL, LOUGHBOROUGH, MANCHESTER, NEWCASTLE, NORTHUMBRIA, NOTTINGHAM, READING, SHEFFIELD
Please check with your university careers service for full details of local events.

MINIMUM ENTRY REQUIREMENTS
2.1 Degree
Relevant degree required for some roles.

APPLICATION DEADLINE
January 2015

FURTHER INFORMATION
www.Top100GraduateEmployers.com
Register now for the latest news, events information and graduate recruitment details for Britain's leading employers.

We Know
OUR

core strengths

WHY NOT DISCOVER YOURS?

GRADUATE SCHEMES - NATIONWIDE

Graduates rate Morrisons in the Top 100 employers. Probably because we make so many into managers. We have an eye for fresh talent. We can spot it in qualities like the ability to move quickly from one challenge to another, respect, integrity, team work and a passion for doing things simpler and smarter. And then we nurture it, treating you as someone to be valued, supporting and encouraging your progress, trusting you to take on new things, showing you how, and being your biggest and best supporter when you succeed. We're a business that's changing fast and can take you far. We know our core strengths so why not discover yours?

To find out more go to **Morrisons.jobs/graduates**

MORRISONS

Newton
The science of performance

Newton works hands-on with some of the best organisations in the world to implement transformational, award-winning change. Their consultants make a difference to the lives of a wide range of people, from top level executives to blue collar workers, NHS patients, and children in social care.

Newton are looking for people that have the entrepreneurial skills and personality to grow with them as they continue to meet the ever-rising demand for real business results.

Graduates joining Newton join an organisation with high expectations. They recruit the brightest minds – people that enjoy meeting demanding challenges and want to work in dynamic, highly rewarding environments across multiple sectors including healthcare, transport, defence, local government, services, manufacturing and private equity.

Newton are looking for people that can quickly take on responsibility, and have the entrepreneurial skills and personality to progress with them. Newton's people drive their business. It's the quality of their work, their technical capabilities and their ability to communicate with colleagues and client teams at all levels that makes Newton exceptional. This is why they've developed one of the most rigorous recruiting processes in the industry.

Newton look for people who have ambition and determination, who are confident, interesting, and enthusiastic. People with outstanding academic backgrounds, first-rate technical skills, and the ability to analyse and solve complex problems. On top of this, they need to be insightful and personable – someone who can mentor, motivate and develop the people they work with.

Newton want people who are not afraid to challenge convention, who innovate and have the conviction to follow through their ideas.

GRADUATE VACANCIES IN 2015

CONSULTING

IT

NUMBER OF VACANCIES
50 graduate jobs

LOCATIONS OF VACANCIES

STARTING SALARY FOR 2015
£38,000
Including a company car allowance and a £4,000 sign-on bonus.

UNIVERSITY VISITS IN 2014-15
BATH, BIRMINGHAM, BRISTOL, CAMBRIDGE, DURHAM, EDINBURGH, EXETER, IMPERIAL COLLEGE LONDON, LEEDS, LONDON SCHOOL OF ECONOMICS, MANCHESTER, NOTTINGHAM, OXFORD, SOUTHAMPTON, UNIVERSITY COLLEGE LONDON, WARWICK
Please check with your university careers service for full details of local events.

MINIMUM ENTRY REQUIREMENTS
Relevant degree required for some roles.

APPLICATION DEADLINE
Year-round recruitment
Early application advised.

FURTHER INFORMATION
www.Top100GraduateEmployers.com
Register now for the latest news, events information and graduate recruitment details for Britain's leading employers.

The ngdp is a two-year graduate management development programme, run by the Local Government Association. The programme was set up to provide local government with the high-calibre managers their communities need and to give committed graduates the opportunity to make a positive impact.

Local government is the largest and most diverse employer in the UK, with around 1.2 million staff in over 400 local authorities and in excess of 500 different occupational areas. Since 2002 approximately 600 graduates have completed the programme, all taking advantage of the wide range of opportunities available with many now holding influential managerial and policy roles. Now is a time of huge change in the public sector and trainees will make a real contribution to shaping and implementing this change.

The national programme framework is built on a series of placements in key areas within a council and offers a range of experiences and challenges. All of which will provide a broad understanding of different aspects of local government in strategy, front-line service and support. Although employed by a participating authority on a two-year, fixed-term contract, graduates will also benefit from being part of a national programme group, giving them the opportunity to participate in a national induction event, join an established knowledge-sharing network and take part in an accredited series of learning and development components.

The programme has taken graduates in many different directions, with many alumni occupying key roles within the local government and the wider public sector. Ultimately, this is a chance to be part of an exciting period of opportunity and not just propose change, but be the one to make it happen.

GRADUATE VACANCIES IN 2015
GENERAL MANAGEMENT

NUMBER OF VACANCIES
100-120 graduate jobs

LOCATIONS OF VACANCIES

STARTING SALARY FOR 2015
£23,188
Plus inner or outer London weighting where appropriate.

UNIVERSITY VISITS IN 2014-15
BIRMINGHAM, BRISTOL, CAMBRIDGE, DURHAM, EDINBURGH, ESSEX, LANCASTER, LEEDS, LEICESTER, MANCHESTER, NOTTINGHAM, OXFORD, SHEFFIELD, WARWICK, YORK
Please check with your university careers service for full details of local events.

MINIMUM ENTRY REQUIREMENTS
2.1 Degree

APPLICATION DEADLINE
January 2015

FURTHER INFORMATION
www.Top100GraduateEmployers.com
Register now for the latest news, events information and graduate recruitment details for Britain's leading employers.

NATIONAL GRADUATE
DEVELOPMENT PROGRAMME

ngdp
FOR LOCAL GOVERNMENT

Real life. Real work.
Your opportunity to **make a difference.**

'As an NMT I am encouraged to challenge current working practices, spot future opportunities and support change in a time of uncertainty. By working on a project which has gained national recognition it has enabled the council to think differently about how it demonstrates change and delivers services in today's challenging environment.'

Jonathan Downs, National Management Trainee, Oldham Council

'This programme gives you access to the inner workings of local government, a sector that is changing rapidly. There are opportunities for innovation around service delivery and supporting communities. I have been able to work in a number of different departments, delivering a wide array of services which affect people's daily lives.'

Michael Gladstone, Customer Service Improvement Officer, London Borough of Sutton

That's what the ngdp is all about. It's a two-year graduate training programme designed to help you develop as a leader in local government, giving you hands on experience and genuine responsibility. You'll take on a variety of projects. You'll meet all sorts of people. And you'll enjoy all the challenges and opportunities.

To find out more about ngdp and why you should join us visit **www.ngdp.org.uk**

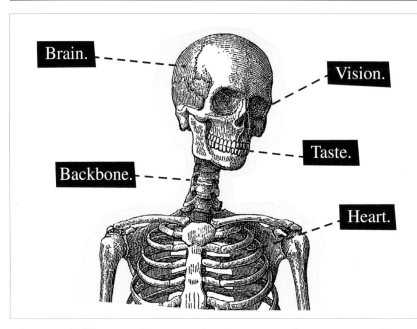

Brain. — Vision. — Taste. — Backbone. — Heart.

GRADUATE VACANCIES IN 2015

FINANCE
GENERAL MANAGEMENT
HUMAN RESOURCES
IT

NUMBER OF VACANCIES
To be confirmed

LOCATIONS OF VACANCIES

STARTING SALARY FOR 2015
£22,500+

UNIVERSITY VISITS IN 2014-15
Please check with your university careers service for full details of local events.

MINIMUM ENTRY REQUIREMENTS
2.2 Degree

APPLICATION DEADLINE
Please see website for full details.

FURTHER INFORMATION
www.Top100GraduateEmployers.com
Register now for the latest news, events information and graduate recruitment details for Britain's leading employers.

The NHS is like no other organisation on earth. Born out of the idea that good healthcare should be available to all, it is one of the world's largest publicly funded health services. It has a budget of over £90 billion and employs more than 1 million people. This makes it the single biggest employer in Europe.

The NHS Graduate Management Training Scheme has placements all across the UK, giving graduates the unique opportunity to embed themselves in a new local community. Lasting up to two years (or two and a half years for the finance programme), it has been explicitly designed to create the organisation's future leaders.

Within the four specialist areas, Finance Management, General Management, Human Resources Management, and Health Informatics Management, Graduates acquire relevant professional qualifications through excellent training opportunities.

Working for the NHS will often mean standing up to high levels of public scrutiny and having decisions closely inspected. The Graduate Management Training Scheme offers a fast-track route to a senior leadership role, which is a uniquely demanding experience. Graduates will need to be tenacious and resilient and able to respond to an ever changing environment whilst keeping patient care at the heart of what the NHS do. The scheme's graduates are committed to improving people's health and the quality of their interactions with the NHS in every area of the UK.

The NHS is passionate about the Graduate Scheme and what it offers. With salary progression, comprehensive training and professional development, the scheme is ideal for people who care about making a difference.

Leadership Academy

Graduate Management
Training Scheme

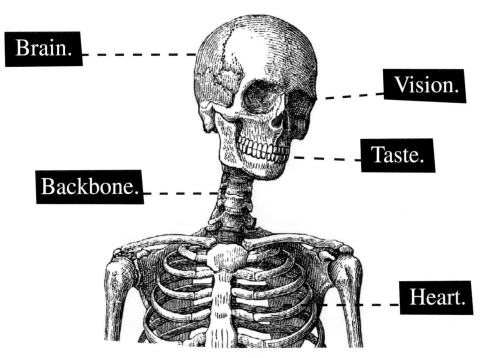

Brain.

Vision.

Taste.

Backbone.

Heart.

Show us what you're made of...

Apply now for the NHS Graduate Management Training Scheme

www.nhsgraduates.co.uk
www.facebook.com/NHSGraduateScheme

^NORTON ROSE FULBRIGHT

Norton Rose Fulbright is a global legal practice. It provides the world's pre-eminent corporations and financial institutions with a full business law service. The practice has more than 3,800 lawyers based in over 50 cities across Europe, the United States, Canada, Latin America, Asia, Australia, Africa, the Middle East and Central Asia.

Recognised for its industry focus, the practice is strong across all the key sectors: financial institutions; energy; infrastructure, mining and commodities; transport; technology and innovation; and life sciences and healthcare.

Norton Rose Fulbright recruits up to 55 trainee solicitors each year. Its training contract is based on a four-seat pattern, allowing trainees to get the widest possible exposure to different practice areas and offices around the world. Trainees have the opportunity to spend one of their seats on an international or client secondment, in addition to seats in Corporate, Banking and Litigation, enabling them to make the best and most informed choice of qualification area.

Each year, Norton Rose Fulbright runs three vacation schemes for law and non-law applicants which are designed to provide an invaluable insight into life and work inside a global legal practice. Successful applicants will have the opportunity to participate in actual work with clients – which could involve anything from legal research to attending meetings or court. Students will also attend training sessions, breakfast briefings about Norton Rose Fulbright's practice areas and social events with current trainees, lawyers, and partners.

Norton Rose Fulbright also runs a number of open days throughout the year for impressive candidates. Open days give prospective trainees an insight into life at the practice. Two of its open days are reserved for first year undergraduates, who will participate in a two-day event which will include work shadowing.

GRADUATE VACANCIES IN 2015
LAW

NUMBER OF VACANCIES
Up to 55 graduate jobs
For training contracts starting in 2017.

LOCATIONS OF VACANCIES

STARTING SALARY FOR 2015
£39,500

UNIVERSITY VISITS IN 2014-15
BIRMINGHAM, BRISTOL, CAMBRIDGE, CITY, DURHAM, EDINBURGH, ESSEX, EXETER, IMPERIAL COLLEGE LONDON, KING'S COLLEGE LONDON, LANCASTER, LEEDS, LEICESTER, LONDON SCHOOL OF ECONOMICS, MANCHESTER, NEWCASTLE, NOTTINGHAM, OXFORD, READING, SHEFFIELD, SOUTHAMPTON, ST ANDREWS, TRINITY COLLEGE DUBLIN, UNIVERSITY COLLEGE DUBLIN, UNIVERSITY COLLEGE LONDON, WARWICK, YORK
Please check with your university careers service for full details of local events.

MINIMUM ENTRY REQUIREMENTS
2.1 Degree
340 UCAS points

APPLICATION DEADLINE
Law: 31st July 2015
Non-law: 28th February 2015

FURTHER INFORMATION
www.Top100GraduateEmployers.com
Register now for the latest news, events information and graduate recruitment details for Britain's leading employers.

Five tips for anyone considering applying to Norton Rose Fulbright.

Don't assume that we are like the others.
We have characteristics and an ethos that make us different to everyone else, so know what those are.

Be totally sure you want to travel and work abroad.
You'll be expected to. If this doesn't appeal, we might not be the right place for you.

Get experience.
It will stand you in good stead for your interview and during those first nerve-wracking weeks.

Be aware of our industry sector-focused strategy.
It's a huge part of the culture and work here, so be able to talk about it during your assessment day.

Apply, and get involved.
Getting through the door and talking to people is the only way to really understand what it's like to work here.

This is what our people had to say when we asked them for some words of advice. If you end up joining us, you'll find that valuable advice will continue throughout your career.

nortonrosefulbrightgraduates.com

NORTON ROSE FULBRIGHT

Progress with purpose

Few organisations offer such a unique opportunity to contribute towards overcoming poverty and suffering. Oxfam has been fighting it for 70 years and graduates can be part of it. Poverty isn't inevitable, so Oxfam gives people what they need to fight it.

Oxfam is one of the most experienced development agencies in the world, working in more than 70 countries. It has run its Voluntary Internship scheme since 2006 and has helped to provide valuable experience and skills to hundreds of people. Voluntary Internships provide a structured, time-bound opportunity, so that graduates can get the most out of volunteering.

Oxfam's Voluntary Internships are based on projects where its people are able to contribute and add significant value to an area of the organisation. Voluntary Internships are usually between 3 and 7 months, depending on the project. Oxfam pays local travel and lunch expenses so that its volunteers aren't out of pocket whilst volunteering.

The roles could be in Oxfam's Oxford Headquarters, a shop or a regional office. They range from Voluntary Assistant Shop Managers, to Marketing & Communications Assistants working in Oxfam's Community Fundraising team, to HR & Recruitment Advisors, to Research Executives in the Campaigns Division. Regardless of whether graduates want to plan a fundraising event, work on a campaign project, or help to run a shop, they will get to experience how a major international Non Government Organisation works and enjoy a friendly, open and passionate working environment.

Voluntary Internships are a great way to learn new skills, experience how a large NGO operates and help to contribute towards Oxfam's goal of overcoming poverty and suffering around the world.

GRADUATE VACANCIES IN 2015
ACCOUNTANCY
HUMAN RESOURCES
IT
MARKETING
MEDIA
RESEARCH & DEVELOPMENT
RETAILING

NUMBER OF VACANCIES
50+ voluntary internships

LOCATIONS OF VACANCIES

STARTING SALARY FOR 2015
£Voluntary

UNIVERSITY VISITS IN 2014-15
OXFORD, OXFORD BROOKES
Please check with your university careers service for full details of local events.

APPLICATION DEADLINE
Year-round recruitment

FURTHER INFORMATION
www.Top100GraduateEmployers.com
Register now for the latest news, events information and graduate recruitment details for Britain's leading employers.

WORLD CHANGERS WANTED

VOLUNTARY INTERNSHIP OPPORTUNITIES, UK-WIDE

Ever wanted to change the world? To right wrongs and make a real difference? Take up an internship that takes on poverty, suffering and injustice, and help us change lives worldwide.

Apply now at **www.oxfam.org.uk/getinvolved**

GRADUATE VACANCIES IN 2015

- ACCOUNTANCY
- FINANCE
- HUMAN RESOURCES
- IT
- LOGISTICS
- MARKETING
- MEDIA
- SALES

NUMBER OF VACANCIES
50+ graduate jobs

LOCATIONS OF VACANCIES

In 2013, Penguin Books and Random House made history by creating the first truly global trade book publishing company. Now Penguin Random House employs over 10,000 people globally across 250 editorially and creatively independent imprints, publishing hundreds of the world's best-loved authors.

In the UK, Penguin Random House UK is home to the iconic Puffin and Ladybird, and literary prize-winning imprints such as Hamish Hamilton and Vintage as well as Arrow – publisher of the Fifty Shades of Grey phenomenon. The company boasts a show-stopping portfolio of authors and brands across fiction and non-fiction: Jamie Oliver, EL James, Nigella Lawson, James Patterson, Lee Child, Peppa Pig, Zadie Smith, Roald Dahl, Mary Berry and Jacqueline Wilson.

Penguin Random House UK shares and applies its passion for publishing the best books with an enormous wealth of experience, creativity and entrepreneurial spirit. It has an open, informal culture where people who love books, ideas and writing can do the best work of their lives.

They welcome the very best talent with opportunities for students and graduates, work experience and paid internships throughout the year. What's more, they can offer employees an unparalleled choice of opportunities to enjoy a long-term, varied and rewarding career in publishing, from editorial to publicity, design to consumer insight, and sales to digital development.

With fascinating transformations happening across the industry, there has never been a more exciting time to consider a career in publishing.

The company has three publishing sites in London: Strand, Vauxhall Bridge Road and Ealing Broadway, as well as regional offices, including its distribution business, employing over 2,000 people nationwide.

STARTING SALARY FOR 2015
£Competitive

UNIVERSITY VISITS IN 2014-15
LONDON SCHOOL OF ECONOMICS,
SCHOOL OF AFRICAN STUDIES
*Please check with your university careers
service for full details of local events.*

APPLICATION DEADLINE
Year-round recruitment

FURTHER INFORMATION
www.Top100GraduateEmployers.com
*Register now for the latest news, events
information and graduate recruitment
details for Britain's leading employers.*

Your Story Starts Here

Finding a great story - editor, publisher, sales director, finance team. Making it look good - designer, copy writer, art director, illustrator. Making the finished book - production controller, product manager, quality controller. Getting it out there - marketing assistant, publicity manager, sales executive, social media manager.

Come and be part of the first of a new kind of publisher that captures the attention of the world through the stories, ideas and writing that matter.

Penguin
Random House
UK

www.uki.experiencepg.com

wecareers.im@pg.com

twitter.com/PGUK   facebook.com/pgcareers

youtube.com/PGcareers   linkedin.com/company/procter-&-gamble/careers

Work every day with lots of

BRANDS YOU KNOW.

P&G

GRADUATE VACANCIES IN 2015

ENGINEERING
FINANCE
HUMAN RESOURCES
IT
LOGISTICS
MARKETING
RESEARCH & DEVELOPMENT
SALES

NUMBER OF VACANCIES
100 graduate jobs

LOCATIONS OF VACANCIES

Vacancies also available in Europe.

STARTING SALARY FOR 2015
£29,000

UNIVERSITY VISITS IN 2014-15
BATH, BRISTOL, CAMBRIDGE, DURHAM,
EDINBURGH, EXETER, GLASGOW, LEEDS,
LONDON SCHOOL OF ECONOMICS,
MANCHESTER, NOTTINGHAM, OXFORD,
STRATHCLYDE, TRINITY COLLEGE DUBLIN,
UNIVERSITY COLLEGE DUBLIN, UNIVERSITY
COLLEGE LONDON, WARWICK
*Please check with your university careers
service for full details of local events.*

APPLICATION DEADLINE
Varies by function

FURTHER INFORMATION
www.Top100GraduateEmployers.com
*Register now for the latest news, events
information and graduate recruitment
details for Britain's leading employers.*

Over four billion times a day, P&G brands touch the lives of people around the world. They reach those who shave with a Gillette Fusion ProGlide or Venus Razor, who wash their hair with Pantene or Head & Shoulders, who wear a scent from Hugo Boss, and who wash their clothes with Ariel.

P&G has one of the strongest portfolios of trusted, leading quality brands, including Pampers, Herbal Essences, Fairy, Lenor, Gillette, Oral-B, Duracell, Olay, Wella, and Braun. The company consists of around 120,000 employees across 150 nationalities, working in 70 countries across the globe.

P&G attracts and recruits the the finest people in the world, because they develop talents from within. This means graduates won't just get their first job out of university, they are being hired with the expectation that they will grow into one of P&G's future leaders. Maybe even the next CEO. New starters with P&G can expect a job with responsibility from day one and a career with a variety of challenging roles that develop and broaden their skills, together with the training and coaching to help them succeed.

P&G hires graduates into permanent roles, following a successful internship/ placement or career academy with the company.

P&G look beyond just good academic records from their applicants. They are looking for graduates who are smart and savvy, leaders who stand out from the crowd, who are able to get things done. They want to hear about achievements at work, in clubs, societies, voluntary and community activities and to see how graduates have stretched and challenged themselves and others.

The commercial functions welcome applicants from any degree discipline. Product Supply (Manufacturing/Engineering/Supply Network Operations) requires a technical degree and R&D requires an engineering or science degree.

We develop the world's best leaders.

How long before it's you?

As a Build-from-Within company, we hire graduates with the potential to become future leaders of our business.

You bring your passion...

...P&G gives you the challenges that will inspire you.

We develop graduates through on-the-job learning experiences and new assignments throughout their career.

This means you do not start on a rotational training programme. You will join at entry level and will have a role with real responsibility and ownership from day one, whilst being supported and coached by your manager, mentor and other colleagues.

find us on
www.facebook.com/pgcareers

Apply now at:
we.experiencePG.com

pwc

The opportunity of a lifetime

Opportunities are at the heart of a career with PwC. Opportunities to grow as an individual, to build lasting relationships and make an impact in a place where people, quality and value mean everything. A career at PwC means to be a part of the world's leading professional services network and enjoy the benefits that come with that.

PwC's continued success, size and scale, not forgetting their extensive client base, creates an environment where undergraduates and graduates get access to the best career and work experience opportunities.

They choose the best people to join them, but it might be surprising to learn they're from a wide range of backgrounds and have studied all sorts of degree subjects. Along with strong academics, PwC are looking for graduates keen to develop, with business awareness, intellectual and cultural curiosity and the ability to build strong relationships, while making a positive impact with their clients and each other.

Graduates get access to the best learning and development around; learning by doing, learning from others and more formal approaches to learning – for instance, a professional qualification. Graduates are in the driving seat of their development, and have the support of a structured career development programme.

For undergraduates and graduates exploring work experience opportunities, or ways to help them decide where their skills, interests and career goals could best fit, they could attend a PwC career open day, or apply to a summer internships or work placement.

Join PwC. They're focused on helping graduates reach their full potential while providing a competitive salary and personally tailored benefits package. Take the opportunity of a lifetime.

GRADUATE VACANCIES IN 2015
ACCOUNTANCY
CONSULTING
FINANCE
IT
LAW

NUMBER OF VACANCIES
1,200 graduate jobs

LOCATIONS OF VACANCIES

STARTING SALARY FOR 2015
£Competitive
Plus holiday entitlement, bike scheme, gym membership, healthcare, an interest-free loan and study support.

UNIVERSITY VISITS IN 2014-15
ABERDEEN, ASTON, BATH, BELFAST, BIRMINGHAM, CAMBRIDGE, CARDIFF, DURHAM, EDINBURGH, ESSEX, EXETER, GLASGOW, IMPERIAL COLLEGE LONDON, KING'S COLLEGE LONDON, LANCASTER, LEEDS, LIVERPOOL, LOUGHBOROUGH, MANCHESTER, NEWCASTLE, NOTTINGHAM, OXFORD, PLYMOUTH, READING, SOUTHAMPTON, ST ANDREWS, UNIVERSITY COLLEGE LONDON, WARWICK, YORK
Please check with your university careers service for full details of local events.

MINIMUM ENTRY REQUIREMENTS
2.1 Degree
300 UCAS points

APPLICATION DEADLINE
Varies by function

FURTHER INFORMATION
www.Top100GraduateEmployers.com
Register now for the latest news, events information and graduate recruitment details for Britain's leading employers.

English
degree

It's the skills
you've gained while
at university, like
communication,
teamworking and
problem solving that
can all lead to a
career with us

We hire graduates
from a huge range
of degree subjects

Your degree
is just
the start

Arts
degree

Science
degree

Last year, almost half
the graduates who
joined us came from
an arts & humanities,
science, law or social
sciences degree subject

History
degree

Geography
degree

www.pwc.com/uk/careers

Rolls-Royce

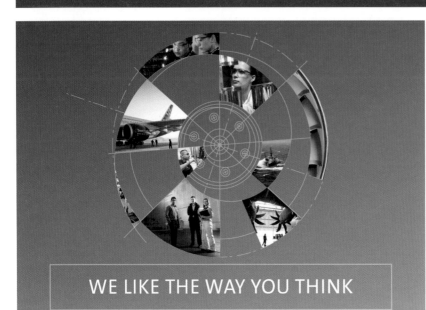

WE LIKE THE WAY YOU THINK

Rolls-Royce is one of the most recognised brands in the world providing integrated power solutions for customers in the civil and defence aerospace, and marine markets. They are the world's second largest provider of defence aero-engine products.

Their marine products are currently on 30,000 vessels, and, at this very moment, 400,000 people are flying in aircraft powered by Rolls-Royce engines. A global organisation with customers in 120 nations, they have an order book worth over £71 billion.

But it's the people at Rolls-Royce who power the business, delivering excellence to their customers and contributing to the continued success of the company. Which is why they look for a certain mind-set when recruiting interns and graduates. They look for people who can see the logical and the innovative, who can analyse as well as inspire – who love to think as well as get hands-on.

Rolls-Royce supports graduates and interns to develop their skills and gain practical experience within a world-class organisation. With opportunities spanning a vast amount of areas – from engineering to customer management - the prospects are huge. All graduates and interns need is well-grounded talent and the ideas to make it work.

Those people joining one of Rolls-Royce's internship or graduate programmes could be involved in the latest groundbreaking innovations and global initiatives. They've enabled land-speed records, developed the world's most efficient aero-engine, designed the world's most eco-friendly ships, and powered nuclear submarines. In pursuit of better power for a changing world, graduates apply their knowledge and skills to develop the best solutions for their customers and the environment.

GRADUATE VACANCIES IN 2015
ENGINEERING
FINANCE
GENERAL MANAGEMENT
HUMAN RESOURCES
PURCHASING
SALES

NUMBER OF VACANCIES
Around 400 graduate jobs

LOCATIONS OF VACANCIES

STARTING SALARY FOR 2015
£27,500
Plus a £2,000 joining bonus.

UNIVERSITY VISITS IN 2014-15
BATH, BELFAST, BIRMINGHAM, BRISTOL, BRUNEL, CAMBRIDGE, DURHAM, EDINBURGH, EXETER, GLASGOW, HERIOT-WATT, IMPERIAL COLLEGE LONDON, LANCASTER, LEEDS, LIVERPOOL, LONDON SCHOOL OF ECONOMICS, LOUGHBOROUGH, MANCHESTER, NEWCASTLE, NOTTINGHAM, NOTTINGHAM TRENT, OXFORD, SHEFFIELD, SOUTHAMPTON, ST ANDREWS, STRATHCLYDE, UNIVERSITY COLLEGE LONDON, WARWICK
Please check with your university careers service for full details of local events.

MINIMUM ENTRY REQUIREMENTS
2.1 Degree

APPLICATION DEADLINE
Year-round recruitment
Early application advised.

FURTHER INFORMATION
www.Top100GraduateEmployers.com
Register now for the latest news, events information and graduate recruitment details for Britain's leading employers.

CREATIVE

innovative

excellence

PIONEER

expert

leader

OBJECTIVE

analytical

LOGICAL

WE LIKE THE WAY YOU THINK

Internship and graduate opportunities in: Engineering, Manufacturing Engineering, Commercial, Customer Management & Services, Purchasing, Supply Chain Management, Operations Management, Finance, Project Management or Human Resources.

We're known the world over for delivering excellence – creating high-performance, integrated power solutions for use on land, at sea and in the air. And now we're looking for minds like yours to help keep our customers one step ahead of an ever-changing world. The kind of minds that can see the logical and the innovative, who can analyse as well as inspire – who love to think as well as get hands-on.

With opportunities spanning a vast amount of areas – the prospects for all kinds of undergraduates and graduates at Rolls-Royce are huge. You'll be given support to develop as an expert or leader in your field. All you need to bring is well-grounded talent and the ideas to make it work. To find out more visit rolls-royce.com/graduates or rolls-royce.com/internships

Trusted to deliver excellence

Rolls-Royce

www.raf.mod.uk/careers

facebook.com/RAFCareers

youtube.com/royalairforce   twitter.com/RAFCareers

With hundreds of aircraft and more than 30,000 active personnel, the Royal Air Force (RAF) is a key part of the British Armed Forces, defending the UK and its interests, strengthening international peace and stability, as well as being a force for good in the world.

People lie at the heart of the RAF and it relies upon their professionalism, dedication and courage to achieve the RAF's vision of being 'an agile, adaptable and capable Air Force that, person for person, is second to none, and that makes a decisive air power contribution in support of the UK Defence Mission'.

The world is a changing place and so is the Royal Air Force; it is becoming a smaller, more dynamic and more flexible force able to carry out its missions. To meet the changing times and challenges, and because of the greater capability of technology, the number of people in the RAF has reduced in recent years.

However, this allows the RAF to focus on the staff they have and ensure that they get the very best equipment and training. Recruiting people of the right quality is therefore a key part of the RAF's vision for the future.

The RAF encompasses all aspects of operations, including the use of the very latest hi-tech equipment but the centre of the RAF's vision has always been its people – and it always will be. It prides itself on attracting the highest quality recruits from all sectors of society and provides first-class training and continuing development.

Officers in the Royal Air Force are expected to lead from the front, setting standards for the men and women under their command. For graduates, there are more than twenty different jobs to chose from including Air Traffic Control Officer and Logistics or Flight Operations Officer, as well as opportunities for qualified doctors, nurses and dentists.

RBS

rbsbankyoubuild.com

facebook.com/rbsearlycareers

youtube.com/RBSEarlyCareers   twitter.com/rbsearlycareers

A career with RBS offers the chance to make a real difference. The international financial services group is changing the way it works and has an exciting vision for the future. For graduates and interns, that means rich and varied opportunities and a stimulating environment.

RBS is building a new bank that will be safer and stronger than ever before. As a result, the business is looking for talented new people who can demonstrate a real sense of ambition and enthusiasm.

Graduates and interns can join one of five core areas: Corporate & Institutional Banking, Commercial & Private Banking, Personal & Business Banking, Services and Support & Control Functions such as Risk, HR and Finance.

RBS is a UK-centred bank with major offices in Edinburgh and London. It supports its customers in accessing international markets in Europe, Asia, the Middle East and North America.

Applications are welcome from candidates whatever their degree subject or level of experience. However, RBS has high expectations of candidates. They'll need to demonstrate strong academic performance, as well as an interest in finance and the immense changes that have been taking place within the industry. Adaptability is highly prized across the bank. They seek to develop people with multiple areas of expertise and the ability to apply them in changing circumstances.

In return for their contribution and commitment, new recruits will benefit from world-class development and early responsibility. Colleagues, buddies and managers will help them achieve their potential and they'll have the opportunity to build important relationships with the wider world through educational, social and community initiatives.

GRADUATE VACANCIES IN 2015

ACCOUNTANCY
FINANCE
GENERAL MANAGEMENT
HUMAN RESOURCES
INVESTMENT BANKING
IT
MARKETING

NUMBER OF VACANCIES

350+ graduate jobs

LOCATIONS OF VACANCIES

Vacancies also available in Europe, Asia, the USA and elsewhere in the world.

STARTING SALARY FOR 2015

£Competitive

Bonuses vary depending on the programme.

UNIVERSITY VISITS IN 2014-15

BRISTOL, CAMBRIDGE, CITY, DURHAM, EDINBURGH, IMPERIAL COLLEGE LONDON, LEICESTER, LONDON SCHOOL OF ECONOMICS, MANCHESTER, NOTTINGHAM, OXFORD, UNIVERSITY COLLEGE LONDON, WARWICK

Please check with your university careers service for full details of local events.

MINIMUM ENTRY REQUIREMENTS

2.1 Degree

APPLICATION DEADLINE

Varies by function

FURTHER INFORMATION

www.Top100GraduateEmployers.com

Register now for the latest news, events information and graduate recruitment details for Britain's leading employers.

Throughout the course of history, a life at sea has always attracted those with a taste for travel and adventure; but there are plenty of other reasons for graduates and final-year students to consider a challenging and wide-ranging career with the Royal Navy.

The Royal Navy is, first and foremost, a fighting force. Serving alongside Britain's allies in conflicts around the world, it also vitally protects UK ports, fishing grounds and merchant ships, helping to combat international smuggling, terrorism and piracy. Increasingly, its 33,000 personnel are involved in humanitarian and relief missions; situations where their skills, discipline and resourcefulness make a real difference to people's lives.

Graduates are able to join the Royal Navy as Officers – the senior leadership and management team in the various branches, which range from Engineering and Warfare to Medical, the Fleet Air Arm and Logistics. Starting salaries of at least £25,220 – rising to £30,314 in the first year – compare well with those in industry.

Those wanting to join the Royal Navy as an Engineer – either Marine, Weapon or Engineer Officer, above or below the water – could work on anything from sensitive electronics to massive gas-turbine engines and nuclear weapons. What's more, the Royal Navy can offer a secure, flexible career and the potential to extend to age 50.

The Royal Navy offers opportunities for early responsibility, career development, sport, recreation and travel which exceed any in civilian life. With its global reach and responsibilities, the Royal Navy still offers plenty of adventure and the chance to see the world, while pursuing one of the most challenging, varied and fulfilling careers available.

GRADUATE VACANCIES IN 2015

ENGINEERING
FINANCE
GENERAL MANAGEMENT
HUMAN RESOURCES
IT
LAW
LOGISTICS
RESEARCH & DEVELOPMENT

NUMBER OF VACANCIES
No fixed quota

LOCATIONS OF VACANCIES

Vacancies also available elsewhere in the world.

STARTING SALARY FOR 2015
£25,220
Plus a one-off joining bonus of £27,000 (subject to specialisation – see website for full details).

UNIVERSITY VISITS IN 2014-15
BATH, BELFAST, CARDIFF, DUNDEE, DURHAM, EDINBURGH, EXETER, HULL, IMPERIAL COLLEGE LONDON, KING'S COLLEGE LONDON, LEEDS, LIVERPOOL, LOUGHBOROUGH, NEWCASTLE, NOTTINGHAM, OXFORD, SHEFFIELD, SOUTHAMPTON, STIRLING, SURREY, ULSTER, UNIVERSITY COLLEGE LONDON, WARWICK, YORK
Please check with your university careers service for full details of local events.

MINIMUM ENTRY REQUIREMENTS
Relevant degree required for some roles.

APPLICATION DEADLINE
Year-round recruitment

FURTHER INFORMATION
www.Top100GraduateEmployers.com
Register now for the latest news, events information and graduate recruitment details for Britain's leading employers.

YOU MAKE A DIFFERENCE NOT MAKE UP THE NUMBERS

ROYAL NAVY OFFICER

Being an officer in the Royal Navy is a career like any other, but the circumstances and places are sometimes extraordinary. With opportunities ranging from Engineer Officer to Medical Officer, it's a responsible, challenging career that will take you further than you've been before. If you want more than just a job, join the Royal Navy and live a life without limits.

LIFE WITHOUT LIMITS
08456 07 55 55
ROYALNAVY.MOD.UK/CAREERS

sainsburys.jobs/graduates

linkedin.com/company/sainsburys in   grad.recruitment@sainsburys.co.uk

GRADUATE VACANCIES IN 2015

GENERAL MANAGEMENT
HUMAN RESOURCES
IT
LOGISTICS
MARKETING
PROPERTY
PURCHASING
RESEARCH & DEVELOPMENT
RETAILING

NUMBER OF VACANCIES
36 graduate jobs

LOCATIONS OF VACANCIES

STARTING SALARY FOR 2015
£28,000-£32,000
Plus an annual bonus based on both business and personal performance.

UNIVERSITY VISITS IN 2014-15
ASTON, BATH, BIRMINGHAM, BRISTOL, CAMBRIDGE, DURHAM, IMPERIAL COLLEGE LONDON, KING'S COLLEGE LONDON, LEEDS, MANCHESTER, NOTTINGHAM, OXFORD, QUEEN MARY LONDON, SOUTHAMPTON, UNIVERSITY COLLEGE LONDON
Please check with your university careers service for full details of local events.

MINIMUM ENTRY REQUIREMENTS
2.1 Degree
The Retail programme requires a 2.2 degree.

APPLICATION DEADLINE
December 2014

FURTHER INFORMATION
www.Top100GraduateEmployers.com
Register now for the latest news, events information and graduate recruitment details for Britain's leading employers.

Sainsbury's is a retailer with over 150,000 people and more than 1,000 stores. They create, develop and sell over 30,000 Own Brand products. They are growing their product ranges into Clothing, Banking, Energy, Pharmacies and Online – to name just a few.

So the first thing that will hit successful applicants is the sheer size and scale. With Sainsbury's training and development behind them, it won't be long before graduates are making big decisions that involve real responsibility. Every day brings diverse, fast-paced and inspiring challenges. They will get exposure to senior business leaders, learn from colleagues and get lots of support from other graduates too.

That's the second thing that successful applicants will notice. The support. Sainsbury's has strong family values and graduates at Sainsbury's grow as a group. Leaders by Sainsbury's is designed with this in mind – in the past, the organisation's graduates have found themselves helping out with homeless projects and challenged to take the lead in fundraising for Comic Relief.

So as leaders for the future and graduates with drive, ambition and initiative, successful applicants will get all the help they need to achieve. They'll help each other to progress, develop networking skills and begin friendships that last a whole career.

Which highlights the third outstanding aspect of the programme: career development. Sainsbury's offers talented graduates the choice of three great programmes. So, whether they're managing a team of more than 100 people in a store; taking charge on the development of a brand new product; or taking the lead on a business-critical strategic project in the Store Support Centre, graduates will thrive on the challenge.

LEADERS

by Sainsbury's

The 2015 Graduate Programme

What does it really mean to be a leader? Leaders by Sainsbury's equips you with everything you need to play a critical leadership role in our business. Maybe you'll lead a fast-paced store team; maybe you'll take the lead in strategic decision-making; or maybe you'll lead the development of a new product. Whichever area you excel in, you'll be at the forefront of a great retailer, inspiring others, gaining recognition and making the most of some wonderful development opportunities.

Find out what it means to be a leader, by Sainsbury's. To apply, visit sainsburys.jobs/graduates

WE STAND OUT BECAUSE OF *YOU*

savills

Savills UK is a leading global real estate service provider listed on the London Stock Exchange. The company employs over 20,000 staff and has 500 offices and associates worldwide, providing all trainees with excellent scope for international experience as their careers develop.

Savills passionately believe their graduates are future leaders and as such make a huge investment in them. Savills' graduates are given responsibility from day one, in teams who highly value their contribution, allowing them to be involved in some of the world's most high-profile property deals and developments.

Successful applicants will be surrounded by expert professionals and experienced team members from whom they learn and seek advice. Individual achievement is rewarded and Savills look for bold graduates with entrepreneurial flair.

This year, Savills are proud to be The Times Graduate Employer of Choice for Property for the eighth consecutive year. Great work-life balance, global opportunities, structured training and a dynamic working environment are amongst the factors which see Savills nominated by final year students as the preferred Property employer year on year.

The Savills Graduate Programme offers the chance to gain an internationally recognised professional qualification. Offering roles within Surveying, Planning and Estate Agency, with over half of the graduate programme vacancies for positions outside of London. Savills' offices are in exciting locations around the UK work with high-profile and important clients. The diversity of Savills services means there is the flexibility to carve out a fulfilling, individual and self-tailored career path regardless of the location.

GRADUATE VACANCIES IN 2015
PROPERTY

NUMBER OF VACANCIES
70+ graduate jobs

LOCATIONS OF VACANCIES

STARTING SALARY FOR 2015
£Competitive
Plus £1,000 on joining, and discretionary annual bonus.

UNIVERSITY VISITS IN 2014-15
BATH, BIRMINGHAM, BRISTOL, CAMBRIDGE, CARDIFF, CITY, EDINBURGH, EXETER, GLASGOW, HERIOT-WATT, KING'S COLLEGE LONDON, LIVERPOOL, LONDON SCHOOL OF ECONOMICS, MANCHESTER, NORTHUMBRIA, NOTTINGHAM, NOTTINGHAM TRENT, OXFORD BROOKES, READING, SHEFFIELD, SOUTHAMPTON, SUSSEX, TRINITY COLLEGE DUBLIN, UNIVERSITY COLLEGE LONDON
Please check with your university careers service for full details of local events.

MINIMUM ENTRY REQUIREMENTS
240 UCAS points

APPLICATION DEADLINE
10th November 2014
The deadline for the Rural scheme is 24th November 2014.

FURTHER INFORMATION
www.Top100GraduateEmployers.com
Register now for the latest news, events information and graduate recruitment details for Britain's leading employers.

A World of Opportunities...

Alex Melligan
Graduate Surveyor – Residential
Madrid and London

Jaspreet Gill
Graduate Surveyor – Retail
Birmingham and London

Alexandra Gumuchain
Graduate Surveyor – Development
Shanghai and London

Hugo Lear
Graduate Surveyor – Commercial
Sydney and London

As a Savills graduate you get to be part of an expanding global firm and learn from leading property professionals

Savills.co.uk/graduates
careerplayer.com/employers/savills/

🐦 @SavillsGraduate

GRADUATE VACANCIES IN 2015

ENGINEERING

FINANCE

HUMAN RESOURCES

IT

LOGISTICS

MARKETING

RESEARCH & DEVELOPMENT

SALES

NUMBER OF VACANCIES
150-200 graduate jobs

LOCATIONS OF VACANCIES

Vacancies also available in Europe, Asia, the USA and elsewhere in the world.

Shell is a global group of energy and petrochemicals companies. With approximately 90,000 employees in over 70 countries, the organisation's aim is to help meet the world's growing demand for energy in economically, environmentally and socially responsible ways.

Shell offers a wide range of career routes. The scale and global reach of the business means they have a huge range of technical, commercial and corporate roles across most types of Engineering, Finance, HR, IT, Contracts & Procurement, Sales & Marketing and Maritime.

The Shell Graduate Programme is open to graduates and early career professionals. Most are from Engineering, Science, Social Science or Humanities courses but, with relevant work experience, other subject areas are welcomed. The structured Graduate Programme gives graduates immediate immersion in their business with real, high levels of responsibility from day one. The Programme is typically 3 years, although this can depend on the area of the business, and graduates usually complete at least 2 assignments within this time. Throughout they receive comprehensive support from mentors, work buddies, the graduate network (Energie) and access to senior business leaders. Students apply to the Graduate Programme by completing an Assessed Internship or by applying to attend a Shell Recruitment Day.

Assessed Internships are open to penultimate year students. They are usually 12 week placements undertaken over the summer. During this time students are supported through delivery of a live project for which they have responsibility. Project topics are determined based on the student's interests and the needs of the business. Shell Internships are very sought after roles that give a fantastic insight into a fascinating business – one that has an impact on everyone.

STARTING SALARY FOR 2015
£32,500

UNIVERSITY VISITS IN 2014-15
ABERDEEN, BATH, CAMBRIDGE, HERIOT-WATT, IMPERIAL COLLEGE LONDON, LEEDS, LONDON SCHOOL OF ECONOMICS, MANCHESTER, OXFORD, SHEFFIELD, STRATHCLYDE, WARWICK
Please check with your university careers service for full details of local events.

APPLICATION DEADLINE
31st March 2015

FURTHER INFORMATION
www.Top100GraduateEmployers.com
Register now for the latest news, events information and graduate recruitment details for Britain's leading employers.

A WORLD-CLASS COMPANY
NEEDS WORLD-CLASS TALENT

Working at Shell, you could be helping us tackle one of the great challenges facing our world today – meeting the energy demands of a fast growing global population.

Shell is a company of firsts, so we're looking for fine minds that thrive on innovation. We need people who want to get involved and make a difference. We believe in making the most of resources, whether that's working to build a better energy future or encouraging people to achieve their potential.

So our graduate programme is designed to allow you to use your talents to the full on a range of major projects. We look to provide day to day responsibilities that will help you grow through experience. Continuous learning is also as an effective way to develop your strengths.

Everyone has a part to play, from IT, HR and Finance to Sales and Marketing, Supply Chain, Contracting and Procurement and Trading. To find out more about opportunities with Shell, visit www.shell.com/graduate

Let's deliver better energy solutions together.

f Shell   in Shell   t Shell_Careers

Shell is an equal opportunity employer

SIEMENS

www.siemens.co.uk/grads

graduate.recruitment.cp.gb@siemens.com

linkedin.com/company/siemens   in   twitter.com/SiemensUKJobs

As the leading global engineering company, Siemens is behind a diverse range of technologies and services, many of which people take for granted in their daily lives. They design and manufacture products and systems from traffic lights and wind turbines, to rail systems and motor drives.

From keeping cities at the cutting edge of technology, to providing greener energy solutions for the way people live, work and travel – Siemens graduates are helping to provide the solutions for a sustainable future.

For those who are looking to develop a career in Engineering or Business, Siemens offer early responsibility, mentoring and continuous professional development. Graduates will be working for a company that's committed to innovation and facing challenges head on. Located in towns and cities all over the UK, Siemens offer a diverse range of graduate and internship opportunities where graduates will be given the freedom to make their mark and use fresh ideas to keep the business at the forefront of innovative technology.

Siemens does not offer a 'one size fits all' graduate programme – individuals join the company in all types of roles and business areas. The Engineering careers on offer are as diverse as the industry itself. There are roles in Renewable & Fossil Power Generation, right through to Metals and Drives Technologies. There are some great training initiatives too, helping graduates reach Chartered Engineer status. Business graduates will help play a crucial role in helping the company run smoothly and the careers are on offer include Finance, IT, Project Management and Sales. So, for those who join as a Graduate Electrical Engineer working in Renewable Energy, or a Graduate Sales Trainee working in Rail Systems, Siemens will offer variety, challenging work and first class development.

GRADUATE VACANCIES IN 2015

ENGINEERING

FINANCE

GENERAL MANAGEMENT

IT

PURCHASING

SALES

NUMBER OF VACANCIES
80+ graduate jobs

LOCATIONS OF VACANCIES

STARTING SALARY FOR 2015
£Competitive

UNIVERSITY VISITS IN 2014-15
BIRMINGHAM, CAMBRIDGE, IMPERIAL COLLEGE LONDON, LOUGHBOROUGH, MANCHESTER, NEWCASTLE, NOTTINGHAM, OXFORD, SHEFFIELD, SOUTHAMPTON, STRATHCLYDE
Please check with your university careers service for full details of local events.

MINIMUM ENTRY REQUIREMENTS
2.2 Degree

APPLICATION DEADLINE
Year-round recruitment

FURTHER INFORMATION
www.Top100GraduateEmployers.com
Register now for the latest news, events information and graduate recruitment details for Britain's leading employers.

SIEMENS

Advancing technology.
Advancing your career.

If you want a graduate career that makes a difference – join us

Siemens is a leading global engineering company and has been finding innovative answers to some of the world's most challenging questions for 170 years.

From keeping cities at the cutting edge of technology, to providing greener energy solutions for the way we live, work and travel – we're providing the solutions for a sustainable future.

Whether you want to develop a graduate career in Engineering or Business, we offer early responsibility and continuous development; you'll be working for a company that's committed to innovation and facing challenges head on.

Head to our website to find out more.

siemens.co.uk/grads

twitter.com/skystartingout 🐦 facebook.com/skystartingout f

Believe in better

GRADUATE VACANCIES IN 2015
ACCOUNTANCY
CONSULTING
ENGINEERING
FINANCE
GENERAL MANAGEMENT
IT
MARKETING
MEDIA
PROPERTY
PURCHASING

NUMBER OF VACANCIES
90+ graduate jobs

LOCATIONS OF VACANCIES

STARTING SALARY FOR 2015
£25,000-£32,000

UNIVERSITY VISITS IN 2014-15
ASTON, BATH, BRUNEL, CARDIFF,
DURHAM, EDINBURGH, EXETER,
GLASGOW, HERIOT-WATT, KING'S
COLLEGE LONDON, KENT, LEEDS,
LEICESTER, LIVERPOOL, LOUGHBOROUGH,
MANCHESTER, NEWCASTLE, NOTTINGHAM,
READING, ROYAL HOLLOWAY LONDON,
SOUTHAMPTON, ST ANDREWS,
STRATHCLYDE, UNIVERSITY COLLEGE
LONDON, WARWICK, YORK
*Please check with your university careers
service for full details of local events.*

MINIMUM ENTRY REQUIREMENTS
Relevant degree required for some roles.

APPLICATION DEADLINE
Varies by function

FURTHER INFORMATION
www.Top100GraduateEmployers.com
*Register now for the latest news, events
information and graduate recruitment
details for Britain's leading employers.*

Delivering Sky's mix of TV that people love, pioneering technology, award-winning customer service and superfast broadband is a real team effort. Across Sky's business, whether in front of the camera or behind the scenes, they're working really hard to deliver brilliant entertainment, products and services to over 11 million customers.

Graduates coming to Sky will be part of a fast-paced business that's changing the game for the entire industry. They're constantly launching new channels, as well as getting record viewing figures for Sky Sports; bringing on board some incredible brand ambassadors in David Beckham and Jessica Ennis-Hill; and investing in exciting shows like "Game Changers" and "The Smoke". Not to mention blazing a trail for technology development with their Sky Go Extra platform and Sky apps all built in-house.

Joining Sky at one of their state of the art offices close to Central London, Leeds or Edinburgh, graduates will be right in the thick of it. Whatever their skills, wherever they join, from day one, they will be part of a network of friendly graduates that stretches right across the business and across the country. Helping Sky do things better than ever, graduates will work on real projects where they'll make decisions that really matter.

And because successful graduates will be doing such an important role for Sky, the organisation will make sure they have everything they need to shine. This includes giving them a structured and tailored plan to progress their career with plenty of development opportunities. What's more, graduates will have access to great rewards such as free Sky+HD and broadband, as well as enrolment in the Sky Pension Plan, health insurance and a wide variety of retail discounts. Join the people behind Sky today.

Join the people behind Sky

Getting big-budget shows onto UK screens is no easy task. It involves a lot of talented people. At Sky, our graduate programmes cover a range of disciplines across our business and technology functions, from finance to software engineering, marketing to management. Whatever you're studying, there's a place for you to shine, just like Jess, James, and Priyanga all have - this is your chance to become one of the great people behind Sky. Find out more at **skystartingout.com**

The Moaning of Life
Available on Sky

It's our people that make Sky the UK and Ireland's leading entertainment company. That's why we work hard to be an inclusive employer, so everyone at Sky can be their best.

SKY | ACADEMY

f facebook.com/skystartingout

twitter.com/skystartingout

SLAUGHTER AND MAY

Slaughter and May is a leading international law firm whose principle areas of practice are in the fields of corporate, commercial and financing law. The firm's clients range from leading multinationals to Premier League football clubs to venture capital start-ups.

Slaughter and May have offices in London, Brussels, Hong Kong and Beijing. They also work closely with leading independent law firms around the world – these are their "Best Friend" firms. They work in seamless integrated teams with the best lawyers around the world. This flexibility enables them to work with their clients' choice of legal advisers and always select the lawyers most appropriate for the matter in hand. They constantly review their cross-border relationships to ensure that they meet their clients' needs.

They have an extensive practice providing a full range of business legal services and expertise in all key industry sectors. Their core practice areas are Mergers and Acquisitions, Corporate and Commercial, and Financing. They also have leading practitioners in specialist areas including Tax, Competition, Dispute Resolution, Real Estate, Pensions and Employment, Financial Regulation, Information Technology and Intellectual Property.

During the two-year training contract, trainee solicitors gain experience of a broad cross-section of the firm's practice by taking an active part in the work of four or five groups, sharing an office with a partner or senior associate. In addition, Slaughter and May offers an extensive training programme of lectures and seminars led by experienced practitioners, along with courses involving discussion groups that cover general and specialised legal topics. Among their lawyers, 24 nationalities and over 60 different universities are represented.

GRADUATE VACANCIES IN 2015
LAW

NUMBER OF VACANCIES
75-80 graduate jobs
For training contracts starting in 2017.

LOCATIONS OF VACANCIES

STARTING SALARY FOR 2014
£39,500

UNIVERSITY VISITS IN 2014-15
ABERDEEN, BIRMINGHAM, BRISTOL, CAMBRIDGE, DUBLIN, DURHAM, EDINBURGH, EXETER, GLASGOW, LEEDS, LONDON, MANCHESTER, NEWCASTLE, NOTTINGHAM, OXFORD, SHEFFIELD, ST ANDREWS, WARWICK, YORK
Please check with your university careers service for full details of local events.

MINIMUM ENTRY REQUIREMENTS
2.1 Degree

APPLICATION DEADLINE
See website for full details.

FURTHER INFORMATION
www.Top100GraduateEmployers.com
Register now for the latest news, events information and graduate recruitment details for Britain's leading employers.

Newton didn't see an apple fall from a tree, he saw **gravity**

AS A LAWYER you'll need to see beyond the obvious. Behind everyday events, many hidden forces are at work: commercial, political and legal forces that, like gravity, exert their influence unseen.

The world is not always as it seems. That's why we like talented people who can think differently. It's also why we welcome applicants from all academic backgrounds who achieve strong 2:1 results or the equivalent.

To find out more about joining us as a trainee lawyer or for work experience, visit slaughterandmay.com/joinus

Great minds think differently

SLAUGHTER AND MAY

TeachFirst

GRADUATE VACANCIES IN 2015

ALL SECTORS

NUMBER OF VACANCIES
2,060 graduate jobs

LOCATIONS OF VACANCIES

STARTING SALARY FOR 2015
£Competitive

UNIVERSITY VISITS IN 2014-15
ABERYSTWYTH, ASTON, BANGOR, BATH, BELFAST, BIRMINGHAM, BRISTOL, BRUNEL, CAMBRIDGE, CARDIFF, CITY, DURHAM, EAST ANGLIA, EDINBURGH, ESSEX, EXETER, GLASGOW, HERIOT-WATT, HULL, IMPERIAL COLLEGE LONDON, KING'S COLLEGE LONDON, KENT, LANCASTER, LEEDS, LEICESTER, LIVERPOOL, LONDON SCHOOL OF ECONOMICS, LOUGHBOROUGH, MANCHESTER, NEWCASTLE, NORTHUMBRIA, NOTTINGHAM, NOTTINGHAM TRENT, OXFORD, OXFORD BROOKES, QUEEN MARY LONDON, READING, ROYAL HOLLOWAY LONDON, SCHOOL OF AFRICAN STUDIES, SHEFFIELD, SOUTHAMPTON, ST ANDREWS, STRATHCLYDE, SURREY, SUSSEX, SWANSEA, TRINITY COLLEGE DUBLIN, UNIVERSITY COLLEGE LONDON, WARWICK, YORK
Please check with your university careers service for full details of local events.

MINIMUM ENTRY REQUIREMENTS
2.1 Degree
300 UCAS points

APPLICATION DEADLINE
Year-round recruitment
Early application advised.

FURTHER INFORMATION
www.Top100GraduateEmployers.com
Register now for the latest news, events information and graduate recruitment details for Britain's leading employers.

Teach First is a charity working to end educational inequality. Since 2002 over 7,000 graduates have joined the Teach First Leadership Development Programme (LDP) in schools across England and Wales and helped change the lives of thousands of young people in low-income communities.

The LDP is a personalised programme encompassing high-quality training, supportive coaching, work experience and a PGCE qualification. The skills and experience gained can be taken forward into any career. That's why many businesses recognise the programme's ability to effect change and develop leaders for the future. Put simply, they know that graduates who can engage, stimulate and inspire in the classroom can handle pretty much any situation in any organisation.

The LDP is a two-year commitment, but Teach First want it to be the foundation of a life-long engagement with their work to ensure every young person has an education they can be proud of. As well as training inspirational teachers in the classroom, Teach First support their network of ambassadors – those who have completed the LDP – to drive forward change in education in influential leadership positions in education, business and beyond.

Some people join Teach First knowing they want to stay in education; some are sure that they don't; and others are uncertain about their plans. All of them find the experience of the Teach First Leadership Development Programme to be powerful, rewarding and enlightening. And all are changed by it.

Apply now and join 2,000 other graduates committed to ending educational inequality. Education has the power to transform lives and Teach First is working in schools across the country to ensure that it does.

Take up the challenge, get involved, Teach First.

TeachFirst

20% of pupils eligible for free school meals make it to university, compared to 86% from independent schools.

Change their lives.
Change yours.

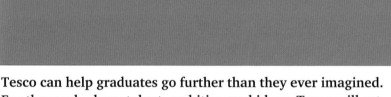

USING OUR
SCALE FOR GOOD
GOES A LONG, LONG WAY.

Tesco can help graduates go further than they ever imagined. For those who have talent, ambition and ideas, Tesco will set them on a career path for life. As the world's third-largest retailer, Tesco's business has all kinds of opportunities and experiences to discover.

Over the last 95 years Tesco has grown from a small market stall selling groceries, to a company with more than 6,500 stores, more than 500,000 colleagues around the world and operations in 12 international markets. And that success is down to having people with the ideas and vision to shape the way the business works. Tesco is looking for graduates who want to continue that success story in all kinds of ways, with new brands and services. It will support them with an on-going commitment to their development every step of the way.

For Tesco, having brilliant people, fully engaged and performing at the top of their game is a no-brainer. So the organisation has made sure the ways they can go about learning and developing themselves in Tesco are second-to-none. That includes support from dedicated graduate trainers, access to a world of learning through their online academy, masterclasses, and even Tesco's very own training app, Academy on the Go, that has a whole range of bite-sized videos on leadership skills!

On top of that, what the company's graduate programme will give its successful applicants is a breadth and depth of experience that will provide the perfect grounding for careers in a variety of leadership roles.

So what does it take to succeed? Tesco looks for graduates who like to get stuck in, who are entrepreneurial and who never give up on a good opportunity. And they should have a good degree (in any subject). Because with their help Tesco can go a long, long way.

GRADUATE VACANCIES IN 2015
FINANCE
GENERAL MANAGEMENT
HUMAN RESOURCES
IT
LOGISTICS
MARKETING
PROPERTY
PURCHASING
RESEARCH & DEVELOPMENT
RETAILING

NUMBER OF VACANCIES
100+ graduate jobs

LOCATIONS OF VACANCIES

STARTING SALARY FOR 2015
£24,000-£30,000

UNIVERSITY VISITS IN 2014-15
BIRMINGHAM, BRISTOL, DURHAM, LEEDS, LOUGHBOROUGH, MANCHESTER, NOTTINGHAM, SHEFFIELD, SOUTHAMPTON, WARWICK
Please check with your university careers service for full details of local events.

MINIMUM ENTRY REQUIREMENTS
2.1 Degree

APPLICATION DEADLINE
31st January 2015
Applications will be dealt with on a first-come first-served basis.

FURTHER INFORMATION
www.Top100GraduateEmployers.com
Register now for the latest news, events information and graduate recruitment details for Britain's leading employers.

JENNIE'S INNOVATION
WAS OUR FIRST GLOBAL HACKATHON

Hackathons are a superfast way to come up with fresh ideas. And in Tesco Labs, where Jennie works, it's all about new ideas. Her idea was to bring together over 350 people from eight different countries and set them about finding new ways to support our customers with cutting-edge technology. What was the winning hack? Well it's still hush-hush but the Tesco Labs team has been heard using words like "Unreal!" and "Epic" and "Far out". Find out how you could make things happen in all kinds of new ways **www.tesco-graduates.com**

A little help goes a long, long way

London brings the world together in one cit...

Boris Johnson

GRADUATE VACANCIES IN 2015
ACCOUNTANCY
ENGINEERING
FINANCE
GENERAL MANAGEMENT
IT
MARKETING
PURCHASING

NUMBER OF VACANCIES
130 graduate jobs

LOCATIONS OF VACANCIES

STARTING SALARY FOR 2015
£26,000

UNIVERSITY VISITS IN 2014-15
BATH, BIRMINGHAM, BRISTOL, BRUNEL,
CITY, DURHAM, EXETER, IMPERIAL COLLEGE
LONDON, KING'S COLLEGE LONDON,
LEEDS, LIVERPOOL, LOUGHBOROUGH,
NOTTINGHAM, NOTTINGHAM TRENT,
QUEEN MARY LONDON, READING,
SHEFFIELD, SOUTHAMPTON, SURREY,
UNIVERSITY COLLEGE LONDON, WARWICK
*Please check with your university careers
service for full details of local events.*

MINIMUM ENTRY REQUIREMENTS
2.2 Degree
Relevant degree required for some roles.

APPLICATION DEADLINE
Varies by function

FURTHER INFORMATION
www.Top100GraduateEmployers.com
*Register now for the latest news, events
information and graduate recruitment
details for Britain's leading employers.*

Transport for London (TfL) is an innovator in transport and its services are now recognised from all around the world. From its red buses and black cabs to Tube trains, TfL is responsible for virtually every mode of transport in the city, and so without TfL London would stand still.

To keep the city moving forward, it will come as no surprise that it takes over 27,000 staff to make it all happen so TfL invests as much in its people as it does in London's infrastructure. There are not many other organisations that give graduates the opportunity to see the impact their work has on the capital city.

They could be engineers or quantity surveyors; go into general, project or information management; have the analytical skills for transport planning or traffic control; or support the business through procurement and marketing. TfL will give successful applicants responsibility early on, no matter which of the schemes that they choose.

TfL is in the midst of one of its greatest periods of investment and that means there are many exciting projects that graduates could contribute to. Work is now under way on Crossrail, a state-of-the-art underground line slashing journey times from east to west London. TfL is making the iconic Routemaster bus a 'green hybrid machine' and introducing low-carbon taxis. Not forgetting the new Emirates airline and the upgrade programme, which is seeing the development of major stations and underground lines.

Whether graduates want to dig, design, plan, manage or explore corporate finance, they can expect all the personal and professional development that they need at TfL. Join Transport for London to help 'Shape the Future of London!'.

Shape the future of London – become a TfL graduate

Take a wider look at tfl.gov.uk/graduates

We want to be as diverse as the city we represent and welcome applications from everyone regardless of age, gender, ethnicity, sexual orientation, faith or disability.

MAYOR OF LONDON

Transport for London

UBS

UBS is a global financial services firm offering wealth management, investment banking, asset management and, in Switzerland, retail and commercial banking. Around the world, individuals look to UBS to provide them with the advice and opportunities they need to protect and grow their wealth.

Leading companies and institutions rely on our financial resources, expertise and infrastructure to help them grow their businesses, manage their risks and invest in the future.

UBS recruits graduates from all academic backgrounds – the humanities and sciences, as well as economics and finance. Because of its global reach, the firm is particularly keen to hear from students with strong language skills. For UBS, degree subject is less important than a graduate's ability to prove they can analyse problems, plan ahead, make decisions, demonstrate sound judgement and communicate with others. The other qualities UBS seeks in graduates are ambition, integrity, a commitment to accuracy and a desire to work collaboratively with other friendly but driven professionals.

UBS's Graduate Training Program offers talented graduates continuous learning in a fast-paced but supportive environment. The programme lays the foundation for a rewarding career in financial services by combining intensive classroom education, coaching from more senior colleagues and on-the-job experience.

UBS is a place where graduates can expect to be stretched long after university. As a global business, the firm offers a world of opportunities for successful applicants to develop their talent – and to be recognised and rewarded for it. Whether it's acquiring the technical knowledge to create the products of the future or developing the skills to be one of UBS's leaders of tomorrow, graduates are encouraged to make the most of their talents.

GRADUATE VACANCIES IN 2015

INVESTMENT BANKING

NUMBER OF VACANCIES
100+ graduate jobs

LOCATIONS OF VACANCIES

STARTING SALARY FOR 2015
£Competitive

UNIVERSITY VISITS IN 2014-15
BATH, BRISTOL, CAMBRIDGE, IMPERIAL COLLEGE LONDON, LONDON SCHOOL OF ECONOMICS, OXFORD, UNIVERSITY COLLEGE LONDON, WARWICK
Please check with your university careers service for full details of local events.

MINIMUM ENTRY REQUIREMENTS
2.1 Degree

APPLICATION DEADLINE
Varies by function

FURTHER INFORMATION
www.Top100GraduateEmployers.com
Register now for the latest news, events information and graduate recruitment details for Britain's leading employers.

You know *what you want.*
We'll help you get there.

At UBS, our internship and graduate training programs are designed to be a springboard for talented students like you. If you are serious about your career and intrigued by international banking, we offer a stimulating, collaborative environment with opportunities to achieve success across many disciplines.

Wherever you are in your academic career, make your future a part of ours by visiting **www.ubs.com/graduates**

UBS is proud to be an equal opportunities employer. We respect and seek to empower each individual and the diverse cultures, perspectives, skills and experiences within our workforce.

Unilever

Unilever, a leading consumer goods company, makes some of the world's best-loved brands: Dove, Lynx, Tresemmé, Sure, Magnum and Hellmann's to name a few. 2 billion consumers use their products every day. Unilever products are sold in 190 countries and employ 174,000 people globally.

Unilever are the number 1 fast-moving consumer goods employer of choice among students in 26 countries. Around the world, Unilever products help people look good, feel good and get more out of life. Their impact is the result of deep thought, hard work, and carefully applied skills.

Unilever want graduates with the will to lead others in driving these brands forward. The Future Leaders Programme (UFLP) helps talent reach senior management. Quickly.

Graduates can apply to one of the following areas – Financial Management, Supply Chain Management, Customer Management (Sales), HR Management, Business & Technology Management, Research & Development and Marketing.

Whichever area they join, graduates will make a big business impact. The two to three year programme (depending on the business area) involves placements across Unilever's UK & Ireland business with responsibility from day one, alongside excellent training in leadership and business. Graduates will learn business fast. Unilever will support them in achieving Chartered status and qualifications such as CIMA, IMechE, IChemE, IEE, APICS, ICS, and CIPD. When the programme ends, they will move into a management role.

Unilever's challenge? To double the size of their business, while reducing their environmental impact and increase their positive social impact. Behind that ambition, and every brand, lie exciting challenges.

GRADUATE VACANCIES IN 2015

ENGINEERING
FINANCE
HUMAN RESOURCES
IT
LOGISTICS
MARKETING
RESEARCH & DEVELOPMENT
SALES

NUMBER OF VACANCIES
50 graduate jobs

LOCATIONS OF VACANCIES

Vacancies also available in Asia and elsewhere in the world.

STARTING SALARY FOR 2015
£29,000
Plus a performance-related bonus every year and a salary increase every 6 months.

UNIVERSITY VISITS IN 2014-15
ASTON, BATH, BIRMINGHAM, BRISTOL, CAMBRIDGE, DURHAM, EXETER, IMPERIAL COLLEGE LONDON, LANCASTER, LEEDS, LIVERPOOL, LONDON SCHOOL OF ECONOMICS, LOUGHBOROUGH, MANCHESTER, NEWCASTLE, NOTTINGHAM, OXFORD, UNIVERSITY COLLEGE LONDON, WARWICK
Please check with your university careers service for full details of local events.

MINIMUM ENTRY REQUIREMENTS
2.2 Degree
300 UCAS points
Relevant degree required for some roles.

APPLICATION DEADLINE
Year-round recruitment

FURTHER INFORMATION
www.Top100GraduateEmployers.com
Register now for the latest news, events information and graduate recruitment details for Britain's leading employers.

Who we are

WPP is the world leader in communications services – including Advertising; Media Investment Management; Data Investment Management; PR & Public Affairs; Branding & Identity; Healthcare Communications; Direct, Digital, Promotion & Relationship Marketing and Specialist Communications.

WPP has over 150 companies setting industry standards and working with many of the world's leading brands, creating communications ideas that help to build business for its clients. Their clients include 351 of the Fortune Global 500; all of the Dow Jones 30; 69 of the NASDAQ 100; and 31 of the Fortune e-50. WPP employs over 175,000 people (including associates) in over 3,000 offices in 110 countries.

WPP Fellowships develop high-calibre management talent with unique experience across a range of marketing disciplines. Over three years, Fellows work in three different WPP operating companies, each representing a different marketing communications discipline and geography. Fellows are likely to work in a client management or planning role, although some work on the creative side of an agency. Each rotation is chosen on the basis of the individual's interests and the Group's needs.

Fellowships will be awarded to applicants who are intellectually curious and motivated by the prospect of delivering high-quality communications services to their clients. WPP wants people who are committed to marketing communications, take a rigorous and creative approach to problem-solving and will function well in a flexible, loosely structured work environment. WPP is offering several three-year Fellowships, with competitive remuneration and excellent long term career prospects with WPP. Many former Fellows now occupy senior management positions in WPP companies.

GRADUATE VACANCIES IN 2015

MARKETING

MEDIA

NUMBER OF VACANCIES
1-10 graduate jobs

LOCATIONS OF VACANCIES

Vacancies also available in Europe, Asia, the USA and elsewhere in the world.

STARTING SALARY FOR 2015
£Competitive

UNIVERSITY VISITS IN 2014-15
BRISTOL, CAMBRIDGE, IMPERIAL COLLEGE LONDON, KING'S COLLEGE LONDON, LONDON SCHOOL OF ECONOMICS, NOTTINGHAM, OXFORD, QUEEN MARY LONDON, ROYAL HOLLOWAY LONDON, UNIVERSITY COLLEGE LONDON
Please check with your university careers service for full details of local events.

MINIMUM ENTRY REQUIREMENTS
2.1 Degree

APPLICATION DEADLINE
6th November 2014

FURTHER INFORMATION
www.Top100GraduateEmployers.com
Register now for the latest news, events information and graduate recruitment details for Britain's leading employers.

WPP
Fellowships 2015

Ambidextrous brains required

WPP is the world leader in marketing communications, with more than 150 companies setting industry standards in Advertising; Media Investment Management; Data Investment Management; Public Relations & Public Affairs; Branding & Identity; Healthcare Communications; Direct, Digital, Promotion & Relationship Marketing; and Specialist Communications.

We are manufacturers of communications ideas that help to build business for our clients, through creating and developing relationships with the people who buy and use their products and services. We do this through a demanding combination of hard work and flair; logic and intuition; left brain and right brain thinking.

The Fellowship was started, 19 years ago, to create future generations of leaders for our companies. Fellows tend to be intellectually curious people who are motivated by the challenges of marketing communications and by the prospect of working at the confluence of art and business. They spend three years on the program: in each year they work in a different WPP company, in a different marketing communications discipline and, usually, on a different continent.

Long-term prospects within a WPP company are excellent, with many former Fellows now occupying senior management positions.

Deadline for entry:
6 November 2014

**Visit our website and apply online at
www.wpp.com**

**For further information ask at your careers
service or contact:**

Harriet Miller, WPP
T: +44 (0)20 7408 2204
E-mail: hmiller@wpp.com

Useful Information

EMPLOYER	GRADUATE RECRUITMENT WEBSITE	EMPLOYER	GRADUATE RECRUITMENT WEBSITE
ACCENTURE	accenture.com/top100	HSBC	www.hsbc.com/careers/studentsandgraduates
AIRBUS	www.jobs.airbus-group.com	IBM	www.ibm.com/jobs/uk
ALDI	www.aldirecruitment.co.uk	JAGUAR LAND ROVER	www.jaguarlandrovercareers.com
ALLEN & OVERY	www.aograduate.com	JOHN LEWIS PARTNERSHIP	www.jlpjobs.com/graduates
ARCADIA GROUP	www.arcadiagroup.co.uk/careers	J.P. MORGAN	jpmorgan.com/careers
ARMY	army.mod.uk/officer	KPMG	www.kpmgcareers.co.uk/times100
ARUP	www.arup.com/careers	L'ORÉAL	www.lorealbusinessclass.co.uk
ASDA	www.asda.jobs/graduates	LIDL	www.lidlgraduatecareers.co.uk
ATKINS	www.atkinsglobal.com/careers/graduates	LINKLATERS	www.linklaters.com/ukgrads
BAKER & MCKENZIE	www.bornglobal.uk.com	LLOYD'S	www.lloyds.com/TT100
BANK OF AMERICA MERRILL LYNCH	www.baml.com/campusEMEA	LLOYDS BANKING GROUP	www.lloydsbankinggrouptalent.com
BARCLAYS	www.barclays.com/joinus	MARKS & SPENCER	www.marksandspencergrads.com
BBC	www.bbc.co.uk/careers/trainee-schemes-and-apprenticeships	MARS	mars.co.uk/graduates
BLACKROCK	www.blackrockoncampus.com	MCDONALD'S	www.mcdonalds.co.uk/people
BLOOMBERG	jobs.bloomberg.com	MCKINSEY & COMPANY	www.mckinsey.com/careers
BOOTS	www.boots.jobs/talentprogrammes	METROPOLITAN POLICE	www.metpolicecareers.co.uk
BOSTON CONSULTING GROUP	www.bcglondon.com	MI5	www.mi5.gov.uk/careers
BP	bp.com/ukgraduates	MICROSOFT	www.microsoft.co.uk/students
BRITISH AIRWAYS	www.britishairways.com/careers	MONDELĒZ INTERNATIONAL	www.mdlzearlycareers.co.uk
BRITISH SUGAR	www.notjustsugar.com	MORGAN STANLEY	www.morganstanley.com/careers
BT	www.btgraduates.com	MORRISONS	www.morrisons.jobs/graduates
CANCER RESEARCH UK	cruk.org/graduates	NEWTON EUROPE	www.newtoneurope.com/careers
CENTRICA	www.centrica.com/graduates	NGDP	www.ngdp.org.uk
CITI	www.oncampus.citi.com	NHS	www.nhsgraduates.co.uk
CIVIL SERVICE FAST STREAM	www.faststream.civilservice.gov.uk	NORTON ROSE FULBRIGHT	www.nortonrosefulbrightgraduates.com
CLIFFORD CHANCE	www.cliffordchance.com/gradsuk	OXFAM	www.oxfam.org.uk/volunteering
CREDIT SUISSE	www.credit-suisse.com/careers	PENGUIN RANDOM HOUSE	facebook.com/PRHCareersUK
DELOITTE	www.deloitte.co.uk/graduates	PROCTER & GAMBLE	www.uki.experiencepg.com
DIAGEO	www.diageo-careers.com	PWC	www.pwc.com/uk/careers
DLA PIPER	www.dlapipergraduates.co.uk	ROLLS-ROYCE	www.rolls-royce.com/graduates
DYSON	careers.dyson.com/graduates	ROYAL AIR FORCE	www.raf.mod.uk/careers
E.ON	eonenergy.com/graduates	ROYAL BANK OF SCOTLAND GROUP	rbsbankyoubuild.com
EDF ENERGY	www.edfenergy.com/graduates	ROYAL NAVY	www.royalnavy.mod.uk/careers
EUROPEAN COMMISSION (EU CAREERS)	www.eu-careers.eu	SAINSBURY'S	sainsburys.jobs/graduates
EXXONMOBIL	ExxonMobil.com/UKRecruitment	SAVILLS	www.savills.co.uk/graduate
EY	ey.com/uk/careers	SHELL	www.shell.co.uk/career
FOREIGN & COMMONWEALTH OFFICE	faststream.civilservice.gov.uk	SIEMENS	www.siemens.co.uk/grads
FRESHFIELDS BRUCKHAUS DERINGER	www.freshfields.com/uktrainees	SKY	skystartingout.com
FRONTLINE	www.thefrontline.org.uk	SLAUGHTER AND MAY	www.slaughterandmay.com
GLAXOSMITHKLINE	www.futureleaders.gsk.com	TEACH FIRST	teachfirst.org.uk/graduates
GOLDMAN SACHS	www.goldmansachs.com/careers	TESCO	www.tesco-graduates.com
GOOGLE	www.google.com/students/emea	TRANSPORT FOR LONDON	www.tfl.gov.uk/graduates
GRANT THORNTON	www.grant-thornton.co.uk/trainees	UBS	www.ubs.com/graduates
HERBERT SMITH FREEHILLS	herbertsmithfreehills.com/careers/london/graduates	UNILEVER	unilever.co.uk/careers-jobs/graduates
HOGAN LOVELLS	www.hoganlovells.com/graduates	WPP	www.wpp.com